CONTENTS

Newsletters

Dear Family,

WELCOME...to the new school year.

I'd like to invite you to join me in making this an exciting and rewarding year for your child. One of the things I'll be asking you to do is share information that will help me get to know your child better.

Throughout the year, I'll be sending home ideas for activities that you can do with your child to reinforce what we're learning in school. Please become involved as much as you can. Studies have shown that children who get support at home in reading and learning do better in school.

Here are two suggestions for things to do at home:

- **Read and discuss books with your child.** Even after children have learned to read on their own, there are many benefits to reading aloud to your child—and to letting your child read to you. Visit the library together so you can choose books that both of you will enjoy.

- **Let your child see *you* reading.** It's important to show your child that you think reading is valuable and enjoyable.

One other thing: I always appreciate having adult volunteers assist with classroom activities. If you can give some time in the classroom or at home with preparation, please let me know.

Thanks for working with me as a partner in your child's education. Together, we can help your child have a successful year!

Sincerely,

_____

Estimada familia:

¡Bienvenidos al nuevo año escolar!

Mi deseo es que juntos podamos hacer de éste un año productivo y divertido. Una de las cosas que les voy a pedir es que compartan conmigo información acerca de su niño o niña. Esa información me ayudará a conocer mejor a los niños.

Durante el año escolar, les enviaré cartas con ideas de actividades que pueden hacer juntos en casa. Esas actividades ayudarán a complementar lo que aprendemos en clase. Por favor, colaboren tanto como puedan. Estudios han demostrado que los niños que reciben apoyo en sus casas siguen mejor en la escuela.

A continuación hay dos sugerencias importantes de actividades que pueden hacer en casa:

- **Lean libros juntos y hablen de lo que leen.** Aunque los niños ya sepan leer, es muy beneficioso que usted les lea en voz alta y también que ellos lean en voz alta para los demás. Vayan a la biblioteca y escojan libros que les gusten a ambos.

- **Asegúrese de que su niño o niña lo vea leer a usted.** Es importante que usted demuestre que la lectura es importante y divertida.

Otra cosa importante: Yo siempre aprecio la ayuda que puedan prestar voluntarios adultos con las actividades de la clase. Por favor, avísenme si me pueden ayudar en el salón de clases, o en su casa, con detalles relacionados a la preparación de actividades.

Les agradezco de antemano por participar en la educación de su niño o niña. Juntos podemos ayudarle a tener un año muy exitoso.

Atentamente,

_____

Newsletter

Nature's Fury

Dear Family,

For the next few weeks, we'll be studying the theme *Nature's Fury*. Your child will read about phenomena that show nature's incredible force and power—volcanoes, tornadoes, and earthquakes. We will see how people respond to these events.

Theme-Related Activities to Do Together

Helping Hands

You may hear or read news reports of natural disasters and the relief efforts that follow them. Discuss these events with your child. Mention how volunteers and rescue personnel save people, donate food or clothing, and rebuild homes. Ask your child how he or she might help.

Shaking Up Facts

To test your knowledge of earthquakes, see if you and your child can answer the following questions: What causes earthquakes? Where are they most likely to occur? How often do they usually occur? For answers, visit the library to learn more about this natural phenomenon.

A Disaster Plan

Are you prepared in case of a natural disaster? Discuss the types of disasters that could happen and ways to prepare for them. Identify items to include in a home disaster kit, important phone numbers to know, and safety procedures to practice. To learn more, visit the library.

Theme-Related Books to Enjoy Together!

Storm Chaser *by Keith Elliot Greenberg. Blackbirch 1997 (32p)* NOAA pilot Brian Taggart flies into the eye of a hurricane to study it and report its progress.

Trial by Ice *by K. M. Kostyal. National Geographic 1999 (64p)* This photobiography of explorer Ernest Shackleton is introduced by his granddaughter.

Earthquake! A Story of Old San Francisco *by Kathleen Kudlinski. Puffin 1995 (64p)* Philip must save his horses during the San Francisco earthquake.

Volcano: The Eruption and Healing of Mount St. Helens *by Patricia Lauber. Aladdin 1993 (60p)* After a devastating 1980 eruption, Mount St. Helens begins to recover.

Night of the Twisters *by Ivy Ruckman. Harper 1986 (159p) paper* A boy and his family struggle to survive a series of destructive tornadoes.

Blizzard: Estes Park, Colorado, 1886 *by Kathleen Duey. Aladdin 1998 (64p)* Maggie must try to save her cousin who is lost in a sudden blizzard.

Tornadoes *by Seymour Simon. Morrow 1999 (32p)* Simon explains how tornadoes form and how we can protect ourselves from them.

Boletín

Naturaleza feroz

Estimada familia:

Durante las próximas semanas, vamos a estudiar el tema *Naturaleza feroz*. Su niño o niña leerá acerca de fenómenos que demuestran la increíble fuerza de la naturaleza: volcanes, tornados y terremotos. También veremos cómo responden las personas a esos fenómenos naturales.

Actividades para hacer juntos

Un poco de ayuda

Hable con su niño o niña acerca de los esfuerzos de rescate que se llevan a cabo después de que ocurre un desastre natural. Pregunte a su niño o niña cómo cree que él o ella pueda ayudar en caso de un desastre.

Conocimiento vital

Pregunte a su niño o niña: ¿Qué causa los terremotos? ¿Dónde es más probable que ocurran? ¿Con qué frecuencia ocurren normalmente? Para hallar las respuestas y aprender más acerca de este fenómeno natural, visiten una biblioteca.

Plan para caso de desastre

Hablen acerca de los tipos de desastre que podrían ocurrir. Hablen de cómo podrían prepararse para ellos. Para obtener más ideas visiten la biblioteca o pónganse en contacto con agencias como la Cruz Roja local.

Libros relacionados al tema que pueden leer juntos

Storm Chaser *por Keith Elliot Greenberg. Blackbirch 1997 (32p)* El piloto Brian Taggart de la organización NOAA, vuela en el ojo de un huracán para estudiarlo y reportar su desarrollo.

Trial by Ice *por K. M. Kostyal. National Geographic 1999 (64p)* La nieta del explorador Ernst Shackleton presenta la fotobiografía de su abuelo.

Earthquake! A History of Old San Francisco *por Kathleen Kudlinski. Puffin 1995 (64p)* Philip debe salvar a sus caballos durante el terremoto de San Francisco.

Volcano: The Eruption and Healing of Mount St. Helens *por Patricia Lauber. Aladdin 1993 (60p)* Después de la devastadora erupción de 1980, Mount St. Helens comienza a reponerse.

Night of the Twisters *por Ivy Ruckman. Harper 1986 (159p) libro de bolsillo* Un niño y su familia luchan por sobrevivir una serie de tornados destructivos.

Blizzard: Estes Park, Colorado, 1886 *por Kathleen Duey. Aladdin 1998 (64p)* Maggie trata de salvar a su primo, quien está perdido en una ventisca repentina.

Tornadoes *por Seymour Simon. Morrow 1999 (32p)* Simón explica cómo se forman los tornados y cómo nos podemos proteger de ellos.

Newsletter

Give It All You've Got

Dear Family,

For the next few weeks, we'll be studying the theme *Give It All You've Got*. Your child will read about people who have worked hard to attain their goals, including figure skater Michelle Kwan, astronaut Mae Jemison, a student in a talent show, and a boy overcoming his fear.

Theme-Related Activities to Do Together

Aiming High

Have a goal-setting session. Set three goals for yourself and ask your child to do the same. List and post your goals on the refrigerator or in another central spot. Once a week, discuss your progress together. When a goal is met, celebrate!

Formula for Success

Identify heroes in the news and in your community. Invite your child to define qualities shared by successful people, such as *hard-working, courageous, smart,* and *talented*. Work together to write a formula for success based on these qualities.

Glory Story

List explorers and adventurers that interest you, such as Christopher Columbus, Amelia Earhart, Matt Henson, or Jacques Cousteau. Brainstorm what you need to become an expert explorer. Discuss the rewards and risks of exploring.

Theme-Related Books to Enjoy Together!

A Blue for Beware by *Jessie Haas. Greenwillow 1995 (64p)* Lily and her mare, Beware, compete in their first horse show.

Abel's Island by *William Steig. Farrar 1976 (128p) also paper* In this delightful fantasy, a gentleman mouse must learn to survive in the wild. Available in Spanish as *La isla de Abel.*

On the Course with Tiger Woods by *Matt Christopher. Little 1998 (128p)* Golf's newest sensation has played the game since age two.

Ice Story: Shackleton's Lost Expedition by *Elizabeth Kimmel. Clarion 1999 (112p)* When his ship *Endurance* is crushed by ice in the Antarctic, Shackleton must do all he can to save the lives of his crew.

The Wild Colorado by *Richard Maurer. Crown 1999 (96p)* A seventeen-year-old boy joins Powell on his second expedition into the Grand Canyon.

The Mozart Season by *Virginia Euwer Wolff. Scholastic 2000 (256p)* Available again is the delightful story of Allegra's preparation for a violin competition.

Tallchief: America's Prima Ballerina by *Maria Tallchief. Viking 1999 (32 p)* The Native American ballerina tells of her life and career in dance.

Boletín

Estimada familia:

Durante las próximas semanas, estudiaremos el tema *Supera tu meta*. Su niño o niña leerá acerca de personas que han hecho grandes esfuerzos para lograr sus metas, entre ellos la patinadora Michelle Kwan, la astronauta Mae Jemison, un estudiante en un espectáculo de talento y un niño que vence sus temores.

Actividades para hacer juntos

Por lo alto
Establezca tres metas para sí mismo y anime a su niño o niña a que haga lo mismo. Hagan listas de sus metas y péguenlas en un lugar visible. Reúnanse una vez por semana para hablar de lo que ha logrado cada uno.

Fórmula del éxito
Identifique personas de su comunidad que sean héroes. Invite a su niño o niña a definir las cualidades que comparten las personas exitosas. Basándose en esas cualidades, lleguen juntos a una fórmula para el éxito.

Historia de gloria
Haga una lista de aventureros que le interesen como Cristóbal Colón, Amelia Earhart, Matt Henson o Jacques Cousteau. Hablen de lo que se necesita para llegar a ser un explorador experto. Hablen de los beneficios y riesgos de la exploración.

Libros relacionados al tema que pueden leer juntos

A Blue for Beware *por Jessie Haas. Greenwillow 1995 (64p)* Lily y su yegua, Beware, compiten en su primera exhibición ecuestre.

Abel's Island *por William Steig. Farrar 1976 (128p)* En esta encantadora fantasía, un señor ratón debe aprender a sobrevivir en la selva. Disponible en español con el título *La isla de Abel*.

On the Course with Tiger Woods *por Matt Christopher. Little 1998 (128p)* La gran sensación del golf ha jugado este deporte desde que tenía dos años de edad.

Ice Story: Shackleton's Lost Expedition *por Elizabeth Kimmel. Clarion 1999 (112p)* Shackleton debe hacer todo lo que puede para salvar a su tripulación cuando su barco *Endurance* se estrella contra el hielo en el Antártico.

The Wild Colorado *por Richard Maurer. Crown 1999 (96p)* Un muchacho de 17 años acompaña a Powell en su segunda expedición al Gran Cañón.

The Mozart Season *por Virginia Euwer Wolff. Scholastic 2000 (256p)* Una nueva edición de la entretenida historia sobre la preparación de Allegra para una competición de violín.

Tallchief: America's Prima Ballerina *por Maria Tallchief. Viking 1999 (32 p)* La bailarina indígena norteamericana habla de su vida y de su carrera en el mundo de la danza.

Newsletter

Dear Family,

For the next few weeks, we'll be studying the theme *Voices of the Revolution.* Your child will read about the American Revolution from different viewpoints, including those of well-known Patriots, Tories, and African Americans who joined the fight for independence.

Voices of the Revolution

Theme-Related Activities to Do Together

What If the British Had Won?

Discuss how your lives might be different if the British still ruled America. Would we have a king instead of a president? Would we have the same freedoms we have today? What would our daily lives be like?

Points of View

Write a series of role-playing letters with your child in which one of you is a Tory and the other a Patriot. Each of you explains your point of view on the war, including your beliefs and how you hope the war will end. Describe how the war has changed your life.

New Conflicts

Visit the library to read newspaper and magazine articles about wars currently occurring in the world. In what ways are they like the American Revolution? How are they different? What causes are people fighting for? Choose a current conflict to tell each other about.

Theme-Related Books to Enjoy Together!

Hannah of Fairfield *by Jean Van Leeuwen. Dial 1999 (90p) also paper* Hannah's family in Fairfield, Connecticut, prepares to send her brother to fight with General Washington's troops.

Samuel's Choice *by Richard Berleth. Whitman 1990 (40p)* A young African American slave must make a choice when only he can help the rebels beat the British.

Can't You Make Them Behave, King George? *by Jean Fritz. Putnam 1996 (48p) paper* The Colonial rebellion is seen from the perspective of King George III, who imposed taxes that enrage the Colonists.

The Winter of Red Snow *by Kristiana Gregory. Scholastic 1996 (176p)* In this fictional diary, a girl tells how her family helps George Washington at Valley Forge.

Songs and Stories of the American Revolution *by Jerry Silverman. Millbrook 1994 (72p)* Scores for piano, guitar, and voice are included in this collection of songs, along with musical and historical background information.

Toliver's Secret *by Esther Wood Brady. Random 1993 (176p)* Dressed as a boy, ten-year-old Toliver slips past British sentries to deliver secret military information for her Patriot uncle.

The Fighting Ground *by Avi. Harper 1984 (160p) also paper* Thirteen-year-old Jonathan, eager to fight the British, discovers that war is not all fame and glory.

Boletín

Estimada familia:

Durante las próximas semanas, estudiaremos el tema *Voces de la Revolución*. Su niño o niña leerá distintos puntos de vista acerca de la Revolución norteamericana. Los puntos de vista incluyen los de "patriotas", "conservadores" y afroamericanos que lucharon por la independencia de los Estados Unidos.

Voces de la Revolución

Actividades para hacer juntos

¿Y si los ingleses hubieran ganado?

Hablen de cómo creen que sus vidas serían distintas si los ingleses todavía gobernaran los Estados Unidos. Hablen de lo que logramos obtener con la independencia.

Diferencias de opinión

Escriban una serie de cartas en las que uno de ustedes sea un "conservador" y el otro, un "patriota." Expliquen su punto de vista con respecto a la Revolución y lo que esperan que suceda en el conflicto.

Nuevos conflictos

Visite la biblioteca y lea artículos en periódicos y revistas acerca de acontecimientos mundiales de actualidad. Escojan un conflicto mundial cada uno y hablen de lo que aprendieron acerca de ellos.

Libros relacionados al tema que pueden leer juntos

Hannah of Fairfield *por Jean Van Leeuwen. Dial 1999 (90p)* La familia de Hannah's que vive en Fairfield, Connecticut, se prepara para enviar al hermano de Hannah a pelear con las tropas del general Washington.

Samuel's Choice *por Richard Berleth. Whitman 1990 (40p)* Un joven esclavo afroamericano tiene que tomar una decisión, cuando parece que solamente él puede ayudar a los rebeldes que pelean contra los ingleses.

Can't You Make Them Behave, King George? *por Jean Fritz. Putnam 1996 (48p) libro de bolsillo.* La rebelión colonial vista desde la perspectiva del rey George III, quien impuso los impuestos que hicieron que los colonos se rebelaran.

The Winter of Red Snow *por Kristiana Gregory. Scholastic 1996 (176p)* En este diario ficticio, una niña cuenta cómo ella y su familia ayudaron a George Washington en Valley Forge.

Songs and Stories of the American Revolution *por Jerry Silverman. Millbrook 1994 (72p)* En esta colección de canciones se incluyen partituras para piano, guitarra y voz, además de información musical e histórica.

Toliver's Secret *por Esther Wood Brady. Random 1993 (176p)* Toliver, una niña de 10 años, se viste de niño y elude a guardias ingleses para entregar información militar secreta a su tío patriota.

Newsletter

Dear Family,

For the next few weeks, we'll be studying the theme *Person to Person*. Your child will read about helpful and sometimes humorous relationships among family members, friends—including animals that do the work of people—and mentors and learners.

Person to Person

Theme-Related Activities to Do Together

Connection Collage
Make a collage with your child that represents different types of relationships. Use photographs and words from magazines and newspapers. Find words or images that show a range of feelings: love, anger, happiness, sadness. Share your collage with others.

A Deed Well Done
Share a story about how you once helped someone. Describe what you did and the response of the person you helped. Ask your child to share a similar experience. Talk about why some people choose to help others while some don't.

At Your Service
Find out about volunteer opportunities in your community. Is there a homeless shelter or food pantry where you and your child can help? Can you volunteer at a hospital? Is there a nursing home you can visit to socialize with the elderly people there?

Theme-Related Books to Enjoy Together!

Beethoven Lives Upstairs *by Barbara Nichol. Orchard 1994 (32p) also paper* When Beethoven moves in, young Christophe writes to his uncle about their strange boarder.

A Letter to Mrs. Roosevelt *by C. Coco De Young. Delacorte 1999 (105p)* When her family faces losing their home during the Depression, Margo believes a letter to Eleanor Roosevelt is their only hope.

Orphan Train Rider *by Andrea Warren. Houghton 1996 (80p)* The history of the orphan trains is combined with the story of Lee Nailing, who rode an orphan train to Texas in 1926 and eventually found a home and family.

The Secret Garden *by Frances Hodgson Burnett. Harper 1963 (256p) also paper* In this old favorite, the arrival of his orphaned cousin dramatically changes the life of Colin, a spoiled, lonely invalid.

Jericho *by Janet Hickman. Morrow 1994 (135p)* While caring for her ailing great-grandmother, Angela develops a new appreciation for the women in her family.

Seth and Samona *by Joanne Hyppolite. Yearling 1997 (121p)* When Samona wants to enter the Little Miss Dorchester contest, her friend Seth wants to stop her, thinking she cannot possibly win.

Unbroken *by Jessie Haas. Greenwillow 1999 (186p)* Now an orphan, Harriet must live with her irascible aunt and uncle.

Boletín

De persona a persona

Estimada familia:

Durante las próximas semanas, estudiaremos el tema *De persona a persona*. Su niño o niña leerá acerca de las relaciones entre parientes y amigos (incluyendo animales que trabajan con personas), y entre mentores y estudiantes, que a veces son de cooperación y a veces están llenas de humor.

Actividades para hacer juntos

Collage de relaciones

Hagan juntos un *collage* que represente distintos tipos de relaciones. Usen fotos y texto de revistas y periódicos. Traten de encontrar palabras o imágenes que demuestren la variedad de emociones de las personas.

Muy bien hecho

Comparta con su niño o niña una historia de cómo ayudó usted a alguien. Describa lo que hizo y la manera en que respondió la otra persona. Pida a su niño o niña que le cuente una historia similar.

A su servicio

Averigüe acerca de oportunidades para hacer trabajo voluntario en su comunidad. ¿Hay algún albergue para personas sin vivienda o algún centro donde reparten comida para los necesitados, en el que usted y su niño o niña puedan ayudar?

Libros relacionados al tema que pueden leer juntos

Beethoven Lives Upstairs *por Barbara Nichol. Orchard 1994 (32p) disponible como libro de bolsillo* Cuando Beethoven llega a vivir con el joven Christophe, éste le escribe a su tío para contarle acerca del extraño huésped.

A Letter to Mrs. Roosevelt *por C. Coco De Young. Delacorte 1999 (105p)* Cuando una familia enfrenta la posibilidad de perder su casa durante la época de la Depresión, Margo cree que escribirle una carta a Eleanor Roosevelt es su única esperanza.

Orphan Train Rider *por Andrea Warren. Houghton 1996 (80p)* La historia de los trenes de huérfanos sirve de marco para la historia de Lee Nailing, que viajó en un tren de huérfanos a Texas en 1926 y allí logró encontrar un hogar y una familia.

The Secret Garden *por Frances Hodgson Burnett. Harper 1963 (256p) disponible como libro de bolsillo* La vida de Colin, un niño incapacitado, consentido y solitario, cambia de manera dramática cuando llega su prima huérfana.

Jericho *por Janet Hickman. Morrow 1994 (135p)* Durante el tiempo que Ángela pasa cuidando de su tatarabuela convaleciente, aprende a apreciar a las mujeres de su familia de una manera distinta.

Seth and Samona *por Joanne Hyppolite. Yearling 1997 (121p)* Cuando Samona quiere participar en el concurso de la Pequeña Señorita Dorchester, su amigo Seth quiere detenerla, porque no cree que Samona pueda ganar.

Newsletter

Dear Family,

For the next few weeks, we'll be studying the theme *One Land, Many Trails.* Your child will read about people who helped shape the United States between the Great Plains and California, including the Lakota Sioux, a pioneer family, an African American cowboy, and immigrants from Mexico and China.

One Land, Many Trails

Theme-Related Activities to Do Together

Tale of the Buffalo

Visit the library with your child to learn the story of the American buffalo. Discuss what happened to the buffalo during the settling of the Great Plains. How did this affect the Native American communities living there? How did it affect the new settlers?

Let's Go West

Think about places in the American West you'd like to visit, such as Mount Rushmore or the Grand Canyon. Take turns describing why you'd like to visit. Are there specific activities you'd like to do there, such as visiting a gold mine or riding a horse?

Who's Got It Made?

How might your life be different if you lived on the prairie in the 1800s? Make a chart that compares life in the two centuries. Include activities such as doing chores or playing games. As you add comparisons, discuss how life is easier today. How is it harder?

Theme-Related Books to Enjoy Together!

Rachel's Journal: The Story of a Pioneer Girl *by Marissa Moss. Harcourt 1998 (48p)* Rachel records her family's adventures on their trip from Illinois to California in 1850.

Ultimate Field Trip: A Week in the 1880s *by Susan E. Goodman. Atheneum 2000 (56p)* Students spending a week at Kings Landing Historical Settlement learn what life was like for young people in the 1880s.

Off the Map: The Journals of Lewis and Clark *edited by Peter and Connie Roop. Walker 1983 (48p) also paper* The story of Lewis and Clark's 1806 expedition is told through their journal entries.

Sodbuster *by David W. Toht. Lerner 1996 (48p)* The rigors and good times of pioneer life are expressed in this collection of diary excerpts, songs, games, and recipes.

Girl of the Shining Mountains *by Peter and Connie Roop. Hyperion 1999 (144p)* At age sixteen, Sacagewea guided Lewis and Clark's expedition and saved their journals.

Black Frontiers: A History of African-American Heroes in the Old West *by Lillian Schlissel. Simon 1995 (80p) also paper* The author focuses on the African American cowboys, scouts, homesteaders, and mountain men of the Old West.

Luke on the High Seas *by Bonnie Pryor. Harper 2000 (192p)* Luke leaves his prairie home to travel by clipper ship with his uncle to the goldfields of California.

Boletín

Un territorio, muchos senderos

Estimada familia:

Durante las próximas semanas, estudiaremos el tema *Un territorio, muchos senderos*. Su niño o niña leerá acerca de personas que participaron en la formación de los Estados Unidos entre las Grandes Llanuras y California.

Actividades para hacer juntos

La leyenda del búfalo

Visite la biblioteca con su niño o niña para aprender la historia del búfalo americano. Hablen de lo que le sucedió al búfalo durante la colonización de las Grandes Llanuras. ¿Cómo afectó eso a las comunidades indígenas?

Vamos al oeste

Piensen en lugares del oeste norteamericano que les gustaría visitar, como Mount Rushmore o el Gran Cañón. Para cada lugar, tomen turnos para decir por qué les gustaría visitarlo y lo que le gustaría hacer allí.

Vidas distintas

¿Cómo podrían ser distintas sus vidas si vivieran en la pradera en el siglo 19? Pueden hacer una tabla para comparar la vida en los dos siglos. ¿De qué manera es más fácil la vida de hoy? ¿De qué manera es más difícil?

Libros relacionados al tema que pueden leer juntos

Rachel's Journal: The Story of a Pioneer Girl *por Marissa Moss. Harcourt 1998 (48p)* Rachel relata por escrito las aventuras de su familia en su viaje de Illinois a California en el año 1850.

Ultimate Field Trip: A Week in the 1880s *por Susan E. Goodman. Atheneum 2000 (56p)* Durante una expedición de una semana al parque Kings Landing Historical Settlement, los estudiantes aprenden cómo era la vida de los jóvenes durante la década de 1880.

Off the Map: The Journals of Lewis and Clark. *editado por Peter y Connie Roop Walker 1983 (48p) disponible como libro de bolsillo* La expedición de Lewis y Clark en 1806 se relata con las entradas de sus diarios.

Sodbuster *por David W. Toht. Lerner 1996 (48p)* Esta colección de pasajes de diarios, canciones, juegos y recetas refleja los rigores y las diversiones de la vida de los pioneros.

Girl of the Shining Mountains *por Peter y Connie Roop. Hyperion 1999 (144p)* Sacagewea tenía 16 años cuando hizo de guía en la expedición de Lewis y Clark; también preservó los valiosos diarios.

Black Frontiers: A History of African American Heroes in the Old West *por Lillian Schlissel. Simon 1995 (80p) disponible como libro de bolsillo* En este libro la autora pone su enfoque en los vaqueros afroamericanos, los exploradores, los colonos y los montañeros del Viejo Oeste.

Newsletter

Animal Encounters

Dear Family,

For the next few weeks, we'll be studying the theme *Animal Encounters*. We'll read about a photographer observing grizzly bears in Alaska, conservationists bringing golden lion tamarins back to the Brazilian rain forest, and a boy interacting with his animal neighbors on a mountain in New York state.

Theme-Related Activities to Do Together

Meeting the Wild

Tell each other about any experiences you have had with wild animals, including birds and insects. Where were you? What happened? Did anything interesting or funny occur? Keep a list of all the wild creatures you've seen and update it.

Creature Quiz

"I'm short, have black and white fur, and will spray you with a smelly liquid if you make me mad—what am I?" (A skunk!) Take turns playing this creature guessing game with your child. While one of you gives clues, the other can guess the animal.

Deer Dilemma

More and more deer are wandering into urban areas. Should we encourage hunting to control the deer population or do nothing and let nature take its course? Discuss the pros and cons of each solution. Can you think of other solutions?

Theme-Related Books to Enjoy Together!

Shadows in the Dawn: The Lemurs of Madagascar *by Kathryn Lasky. Harcourt 1998 (64p)* Primatologist Alison Jolly and her assistants study a troop of lemurs in Madagascar, the only place where all thirty species of lemur can be found.

Wildlife Rescue: The Work of Dr. Kathleen Ramsey *by Jennifer Owings Dewey. Boyds Mills (64p) paper* Dr. Kathleen Ramsey, her assistants, and volunteers care for injured wild animals at the Wildlife Center in Espanola, New Mexico.

Wild Horses I Have Known *by Hope Ryden. Clarion 1999 (90p)* The author studies the wild mustangs of the Pryor Mountain Wild Horse Range along the Wyoming-Montana border.

Once a Wolf *by Stephen R. Swinburne. Houghton 1999 (48p)* Wildlife biologists work to bring the gray wolf back to Yellowstone National Park.

The Snake Scientist *by Sy Montgomery. Houghton 1999 (48p)* Dr. Robert Mason, recipient of the National Science Foundation's Young Investigator's Award, has studied Canada's fascinating red-sided garter snake for fifteen years.

Julie of the Wolves *by Jean Craighead George. Harper 1972 (180p) also paper* When Julie becomes lost on the Alaskan tundra, she is protected by a pack of wolves.

Boletín

Estimada familia:

Durante las próximas semanas, estudiaremos el tema *Vida salvaje*. Leeremos acerca de un fotógrafo que observa osos grises en Alaska, conservacionistas que devuelven micos dorados a la selva y las relaciones que establece un niño con los animales vecinos en una montaña.

Vida salvaje

Actividades para hacer juntos

Encuentros salvajes

Tomen turnos contándose experiencias que han tenido con animales salvajes. ¿Ocurrió algo interesante o divertido? Hagan una lista de todos los animales salvajes que hayan visto y añadan animales con el tiempo.

Prueba de conocimiento

"Soy bajito, mi piel es negra y blanca, y si me enojas te echaré un líquido de mal olor. ¿Quién soy?" (¡Un zorrillo!) Tomen turnos para jugar a este juego. Mientras uno da las pistas, el otro trata de adivinar de qué animal se trata.

Dilema de venados

Cada día más venados entran a áreas urbanas. Algunos piensan que deberíamos aumentar la caza de venados para controlar el crecimiento de su población. ¿Pueden pensar en otras soluciones posibles?

Libros relacionados al tema que pueden leer juntos

Shadows in the Dawn: The Lemurs of Madagascar *por Kathryn Lasky. Harcourt 1998 (64p)* Alison Jolly, una experta en el estudio de los primates, y sus asistentes estudian un grupo de lémures en Madagascar, el único lugar en donde se pueden encontrar todas las especies de estos animales.

Wildlife Rescue: The Work of Dr. Kathleen Ramsey *por Jennifer Owings Dewey. Boyds Mills (64p) libro de bolsillo* La Dra. Kathleen Ramsey, sus asistentes y voluntarios cuidan de animales salvajes lesionados en el Wildlife Center en Espanola, Nuevo México.

Wild Horses I Have Known *por Hope Ryden. Clarion 1999 (90p)* La autora estudia los mustangos salvajes de Pryor Mountain Wild Horse Range, a lo largo de la frontera entre Wyoming y Montana.

Once a Wolf *por Stephen R. Swinburne. Houghton 1999 (48p)* Biólogos especialistas en la vida salvaje trabajan para volver a introducir el lobo gris al parque nacional de Yellowstone.

The Snake Scientist *por Sy Montgomery. Houghton 1999 (48p)* El Dr. Robert Mason, que recibió el *Young Investigator's Award* (Premio para investigadores jóvenes) de la Fundación Nacional de Ciencias, ha estudiado durante 15 años la fascinante culebra de lado rojizo.

Julie of the Wolves *por Jean Craighead George. Harper 1972 (180p) disponible como libro de bolsillo* Cuando Julie se pierde en la tundra de Alaska, una manada de lobos la protege.

Selection Summaries

Earthquake Terror

As *Earthquake Terror* begins, Jonathan and his sister Abby are camping with their parents on Magpie Island. When their mother breaks her ankle, their father must rush her to the hospital. Jonathan stays behind on the island with Abby, who uses a walker, and their dog, Moose.

Not long after the parents leave, Moose begins pacing back and forth, barking loudly, and shaking the way he does during a thunderstorm. Jonathan notices how quiet everything is — no birds chirping, no leaves moving.

Suddenly, there is a loud noise in the distance. Jonathan feels a jolt and falls forward. He feels the ground moving underneath him. It's an earthquake!

Jonathan feels as if he's riding a surfboard. He and Abby both fall, and she loses her walker. Thinking about the earthquake drills that he practices in school every year, Jonathan tells Abby to put her hands over her head. He tries to crawl over to her but can't keep his balance. Everything is moving, Abby is screaming, Moose is barking, and the earth sounds like a pounding drum. A huge redwood falls, just missing Jonathan by a few feet. It lands on another fallen tree.

Finally, Jonathan reaches Abby. He tells her that they need to find shelter. They manage to crawl over and wedge themselves into the space between the redwood and the other tree. Moose joins them there.

Then, as quickly as it started, everything stops. Jonathan isn't sure how long the earthquake lasted. Everything is quiet again. The children come out from under the tree. They are both okay, except for a few cuts. They know that they are lucky to be alive.

Eye of the Storm: Chasing Storms with Warren Faidley

Eye of the Storm is about storm chaser and weather photographer Warren Faidley. Faidley crosses the United States each year, following lightning storms, hurricanes, and tornadoes to capture them on film for his photo agency, Weatherstock. He became world-famous after photographing a lightning bolt that was the closest ever filmed.

Faidley follows weather patterns that happen at the same time, in the same areas, every year. In the summer, he stays near Arizona to photograph lightning storms in the desert. In the spring, he travels to Tornado Alley, which includes northern Texas, Oklahoma, Kansas, and Missouri. Faidley spends about six weeks there, tracking thunderstorms and looking for tornadoes. His truck, Shadow Chaser, has a video camera, radios, scanners, emergency flashing lights, electronic equipment, and a lot of maps.

Faidley writes in his diary about what happened one May day in Texas. For the first part of the day, he and his partner, Tom Willett, listen to weather reports and go to the National Weather Service for updates, to predict where the storms will be.

Faidley and Willett drive north toward a spot where a funnel cloud has been reported. After a few close calls, they see a white funnel cloud coming down. When it touches the ground, it becomes a tornado.

Faidley sets up his camera and takes pictures. There are two huge storms coming together and creating more tornadoes in the area. Through the evening, the storm chasers follow the storms into Oklahoma. Soon, it gets too dark to take any more photos. By the end of the day they have seen a total of seven tornadoes! Fortunately, there are no reports of any injuries.

Volcanoes

The nonfiction selection *Volcanoes* discusses volcanoes in myth and legend, and then explains how volcanoes form and what causes them to erupt, or pour out lava and ash.

The earth is made up of layers of rock. The top layers are called the earth's crust. Deep below the crust, it is hot enough to melt some of the rock, forming magma. Volcanoes form where there are cracks or holes in the crust. Magma pushes up through the cracks, causing an eruption. The hot magma that pours out is called lava. When the lava cools, it hardens into rock. Thick lava that moves slowly hardens into sharp rocks. Thin lava that moves quickly forms smooth rocks.

The earth's crust is broken into huge pieces called plates. Most volcanoes erupt in places where two plates come together, especially along the rim of the Pacific Ocean. There are under-water volcanoes, too. When they erupt, they can grow high enough to stick up out of the ocean and form islands, like Surtsey in Iceland and Mauna Loa in Hawaii.

There are four different types of volcanoes. Shield volca-noes, like Mauna Loa, have gentle slopes. Cinder cone volca-noes look like upside-down ice cream cones. Most volcanoes are composite or strato-volcanoes. They are formed when lava cov-ers layers of cinder and ash. The last kind of volcano is a dome volcano. Its thick lava creates a steep, dome-like shape.

When volcanoes do not erupt anymore, they are considered extinct. An example is Crater Lake in Oregon.

The explosion of Mount St. Helens in 1980 shows how destructive an eruption can be. But volcanic eruptions can also create new mountains, islands, and soil.

Michelle Kwan: Heart of a Champion

Michelle Kwan: Heart of a Champion is the autobiography of ice skater Michelle Kwan. At the age of twelve, hoping to enter the Olympics, Kwan decides to move from skating at the Junior level to the Senior level. It is a big change, and she needs to pass a skating test to do it. Her coach, Frank Carroll, doesn't think that she is ready. But Kwan doesn't want to wait. While Carroll is away, she takes the skating test and passes.

When Carroll comes back, Kwan tells him what she has done. He is furious at first. Then he tells her that she is going to have to work harder than ever to make her skating artistic.

Kwan's parents are worried that there will be too much pressure at the next level, but they support her decision. Kwan feels ready for the challenge. She knows she will be compared to the best skaters in the world. She is a good jumper, but she is young, and her programs have been easy.

Each skater has two programs to skate: the *technical* or *short program* and the *freeskate* or *long program*, which counts for more of the score. Skaters must perform certain moves in each program: spirals, spins, and jumps. If a skater doesn't do some of them or makes a mistake, the judges take away points.

A skater needs to be strong in body and mind. There is at least one big competition every month. Practicing takes a lot of hard work, and skaters spend a lot of time in the gym, on the ice, and traveling. They are very sore at the end of the day. Kwan also has to go to school and do her homework.

Kwan tries hard to remember that skating isn't the only important part of her life. School is very important and so are family and friends. The real challenge is to keep in mind both the skater and the person she wants to be.

La Bamba

Manuel, the main character in *La Bamba*, is nervous about his performance for the school talent show. His act is a pantomime of the popular song "La Bamba." He will dance and pretend to sing as the song is played on a record player. During rehearsal, he accidentally drops his forty-five record on the floor.

On the night of the show, Manuel waits backstage for his turn. First, two children dressed as a tooth and a toothbrush perform. Next, a violin duo plays. Then a group of girls jumps rope. After them, a boy comes out and performs karate moves.

Finally, it's Manuel's turn to step into the limelight. As the record starts playing, he pretends to sing. Then he tries a few dance moves. The audience goes wild. But something horrible happens: the record gets stuck! It must have been scratched when Manuel dropped it. He has to perform the same part of the song over and over.

Finally, the record player is turned off and Manuel runs offstage, completely embarrassed. Later when he comes out to take a bow, he is surprised that the audience cheers loudly. Everyone thinks he is funny and clever. Classmates want to know how he got the record to stick. Manuel loves the attention. He lets everyone think that he planned the accident.

The Fear Place

In *The Fear Place*, Doug Grillo and his family are camping in the Colorado Rockies. Doug's parents have left on an emergency. His brother, Gordie, has gone off alone after he and Doug argue. Doug worries when Gordie doesn't come back after three days. He sets off to find Gordie, even though he knows that he will have to cross his Fear Place — a narrow ledge that terrifies him.

As Doug follows the rocky trail, he gets more and more nervous. He tries to keep his mind on other things, thinking about animals and rocks. He hears a noise behind him. It is Charlie, a cougar that he has befriended. Charlie moves in front of Doug and she looks back to see if Doug is following.

The further Doug climbs, the narrower the path becomes. His heart is pounding. He remembers the time before when he was on this path with his family. He was too scared to make it all the way across. Suddenly, he rounds a corner and comes to the ledge he is so afraid of. Doug doesn't think that he can cross the ledge. It is narrower than he had remembered. One slip, and he will fall off the cliff.

Doug tries to imagine the ledge as a yard-wide line drawn in chalk. But it is the cougar who shows him how to get around it. She stays close to the side of the mountain and doesn't lean. Doug feels his body tighten with fear. He takes a deep breath. He can't look down. Carefully following Charlie, he reaches a wider part of the path at last.

He has made it past his Fear Place!

Mae Jemison: Space Scientist

In 1992, Mae Jemison became the first African American woman in space, aboard the space shuttle *Endeavour*. *Mae Jemison: Space Scientist* tells about the years of hard work and training it took for her to become an astronaut.

Jemison was born in 1956 and grew up in Chicago, Illinois. As a child she loved to work on science projects and wanted to become a doctor. After college and medical school, Jemison realized her dream. As part of her medical training, she traveled to many countries, including Cuba, Kenya, and Thailand. She liked traveling so much that she joined the Peace Corps.

After she came back to the United States, Jemison applied to the National Aeronautics and Space Administration (NASA) to become an astronaut. Two thousand people applied, and she was one of only fifteen people to be accepted.

Jemison moved to Houston, Texas, to begin her training. She learned about the equipment she would need to use in space as well as survival skills. She also learned what it would feel like to be without gravity. She received the title of mission specialist.

At last, on September 12, 1992, *Endeavour* took off on its mission. The crew stayed in space for almost eight days, performing many scientific experiments. They traveled over three million miles and orbited the earth 127 times!

After leaving NASA, Jemison formed her own company, The Jemison Group. It finds ways to use science and technology to improve peoples' lives.

And Then What Happened, Paul Revere?

And Then What Happened, Paul Revere? tells the story of Paul Revere and his famous ride on April 18, 1775, the beginning of the Revolutionary War.

Revere and his family lived in Boston, Massachusetts. He was a silversmith, a church bell ringer, and a dentist. Then he joined the Sons of Liberty to protest British laws and became an express rider, spreading news between Boston and Philadelphia. He was also a secret agent, trying to find out the plans of British soldiers in Boston.

On the night of April 18, the British began a march to the towns of Lexington and Concord. Revere's job was to warn people to defend themselves. He had to tell Patriot leaders John Hancock and Samuel Adams, too.

Revere saw the signal, two lanterns in a church steeple, that meant the British were sailing across the harbor. He rowed across the Charles River to where a horse was waiting and began his famous ride. He galloped along the Lexington road, waking people up by shouting and banging on their doors.

At one point, six English officers arrested Revere, but later they let him go, without his horse. Revere walked back to Lexington, where he found Hancock and Adams. About fifty farmers had gathered to take a stand against the British. The British troops arrived. A battle began. The battles of Lexington and Concord were the first in the Revolutionary War.

At the end of the war Revere went back to being a silversmith and opened a hardware store. He also made church bells. But he will always be remembered for his Big Ride.

Katie's Trunk

Katie's Trunk tells about the family of Katie Gray at the beginning of the American Revolution. Katie's parents are Tories; they support the British king. Katie's family has lost rebel friends who are against the British. Her friend Celia Warren doesn't speak to her anymore.

One day, Katie's father comes running to tell his family to get out of the house and hide. The rebels are coming. Scared, they run into the woods. Katie feels like a trapped animal. Then she gets so angry that she runs back into the house. She doesn't want anyone to damage the house or the things in it.

Katie runs into her parents' room and hides in her mother's wedding trunk under a pile of clothes. She can hear footsteps and doors slamming. She hears the rebels throwing things on the floor and Celia Warren's father telling the others to look for money.

Katie can hardly breathe inside the trunk. Then Mr. Warren opens the lid. She breathes in the fresh air. The dresses on top of Katie move, and she feels Mr. Warren's hand. Katie wants to scream, but she knows she must keep quiet. After touching her, Mr. Warren shouts to the others that the Tories are coming and that they should leave the house. He leaves the trunk lid open.

Katie comes out of the trunk and begins to cry. Her family runs inside. Her mother hugs her but is angry that she ran back into the house. Katie knows that Mr. Warren called the others away to keep her safe, leaving the lid open for her to breathe. She believes that there is still some goodness in her neighbors, even with the war beginning.

Selection Summaries

James Forten

James Forten is a biography of James Forten, a sailor at the end of the American Revolution and a sailmaker and fighter against slavery afterwards. Forten lived in Philadelphia, home to hundreds of free African Americans and abolitionist groups, including Quakers, who wanted to end slavery. He went to a school that a Quaker founded for African American children.

Forten wanted to join the fight for America's freedom. In 1781, at age fourteen, he went to sea. His job was to bring gunpowder up from below deck during battles. In his second battle, Forten's ship, the *Royal Louis*, was trapped by three British ships. The *Royal Louis* surrendered. Its crew was taken aboard the British ship, the *Amphyon*. Forten was afraid that he would be sent to the West Indies and sold into slavery.

The son of the captain of the *Amphyon* joined the American boys in a game of marbles and befriended Forten. Instead of going to the West Indies, Forten was sent to the British prison ship, the *Jersey*. He felt that his friendship with the captain's son saved him from slavery.

Life for the prisoners was awful on the *Jersey*, but in two weeks, news arrived that the British army had surrendered to George Washington, ending the war. Washington did not approve of sending prisoners to the West Indies. This news, not the game of marbles, is what probably saved Forten from life as a slave.

After the war, Forten went into the sailmaking business where his father had worked. He took over that business and became one of the richest men in Philadelphia. He also became an important abolitionist, speaking out against slavery.

Mariah Keeps Cool

As *Mariah Keeps Cool* begins, Mariah and her friends, the Friendly Five, are busy getting ready for a big swim meet with their coach and friend, Brandon. They are also planning a surprise birthday party for Mariah's sister, Lynn. Because Lynn is a volunteer at a homeless shelter, Mariah asks the guests to bring food and clothing donations instead of gifts.

Mariah is also growing closer to her half-sister, Denise, who is helping them make paper flowers and other party decorations at Brandon's house.

When Lynn shows up at Brandon's house unexpectedly, the girls have to think fast. Denise hides and the Friendly Five hurry to Brandon's pool and pretend that they are practicing for the swim meet. Brandon tells Lynn that she needs to leave so they can practice.

On the day of Lynn's birthday, Mariah needs to get Lynn out of the house. But Lynn just wants to stay in bed all day. Her mom finally gets her out of bed by offering to take her to a bookstore. As soon as they leave, Mariah calls the guests to come over. By the afternoon, everyone is in the backyard decorating and setting up.

Mariah tells all the guests to be quiet as her mother and Lynn pull into the driveway. Then Lynn appears and everyone yells, "Surprise!" Lynn is moved and happy when she sees all the donations for the homeless shelter. Then the party gets underway with music and dancing, and everyone has a great time.

Mom's Best Friend

Mom's Best Friend tells about the relationship between Leslie's mom, who is blind, and her new dog guide, Ursula. Mom's first dog guide, Marit, had become a part of the family before she died. Now Mom needs to find a replacement for Marit.

Mom travels to the same place where she got Marit — The Seeing Eye, in New Jersey. It is a training center where people teach dogs to be guides and teach blind people how to use the dogs. Mom meets Ursula, her new German shepherd, and stays for a month to train with her. At first, Ursula forgets some of her training. Mom has to correct her and try again. Every day they go on walks together to practice her training.

While she is away, Mom writes to the rest of the family about her progress and about the people she meets at The Seeing Eye. Meanwhile, Leslie, her father, and her brother struggle to keep up with the chores around the house.

When Mom and Ursula come home, the dog is friendly but nervous. Mom teaches Ursula different walking routes around town and gives her obedience training. The rest of the family can only watch as Mom plays with Ursula. Ursula and Mom have to become attached to one another first. After a lot of training at her new home, Ursula is allowed to play with the rest of the family. They learn to love her as much as Mom does.

Yang the Second and Her Secret Admirers

Yang the Second and Her Secret Admirers is about the Yang family's oldest daughter, Yinglan, and a trick that her younger brother and sister play on her.

Ever since she and her family moved to the United States from China, Yinglan has shown no interest in making American friends. Her younger brother and sister, Yingtao and Yingmei, decide to make new friends for her. With the help of their friend, Kim, they set out to make her think that her classmate, Paul Eng, has a crush on her.

First, while washing dishes after dinner, her brother and sister wait until they are sure that Yinglan is nearby. Then, in a loud whisper, they talk about how Paul really likes Yinglan and wants to know if she goes on dates with boys. Yinglan stops by the stairs to listen. None of what they are saying is true, but from the slow way she goes upstairs, they can tell that she is thinking about what they said.

Next, they need to get Paul Eng to think that Yinglan likes *him*. Their big chance comes when they are at a science museum with Kim. They see Paul. Quickly moving behind a dinosaur display where he can overhear them, they talk about how much Yinglan likes Paul.

When they see another girl with Paul, the three worry that he has a girlfriend. But Paul comes over to them and introduces the girl as his sister, Melanie. Better yet, Paul nervously asks them if Yinglan ever goes out with boys.

Their plan has worked!

Dear Mr. Henshaw

Dear Mr. Henshaw is the story of Leigh Botts, told in his own words through entries in Leigh's diary. In the second grade, Leigh began writing to Boyd Henshaw, his favorite author. Those letters led to the diary he now keeps. Leigh's parents are divorced, and Leigh doesn't see much of his dad, a truck driver who is almost always traveling.

At school, Leigh decides to enter a writing contest. The top winners get to have lunch with a famous author. At first, Leigh tries to write an imaginary story, but he doesn't like any of his ideas. He then decides to write about a time when he rode in his dad's truck while his dad was delivering grapes.

A few days later, Leigh finds out that his story has received Honorable Mention in the writing contest. At first he is disappointed that he wasn't one of the top winners. Then he learns that he can have lunch with the author, too.

During lunch, Leigh sits across from Angela Badger, the author. She asks him what he wrote for the contest. When she discovers that he is the author of *A Day on Dad's Rig*, she tells him how much she liked it. She encourages him to keep writing. Leigh is especially pleased that she has called him an author.

Leigh is very proud of himself. That night, he writes a letter to Mr. Henshaw to share the good news about his writing.

A Boy Called Slow

A Boy Called Slow is a true story that begins in 1831, when the family of Returns Again, of the Hunkpapa band of the Lakota Sioux, welcomes the birth of a baby boy. His parents decide to name the baby Slon–he, or Slow, because he never does anything quickly.

Growing up, Slow does not like his name. But he can only earn a new name by having a powerful dream or by doing something brave. Slow's father, Returns Again, has earned his name for bravery in battle against the Sioux's enemy, the Crow. Returns Again can also understand the speech of animals. He gained four more names after hearing those names spoken to him by a bull buffalo.

One night, at the age of fourteen, Slow hears that his father and others are going to raid the Crow for horses. Slow goes with them, making his father proud. The men get ready for the fight. They paint their horses and their faces, and take out their coup sticks, lances, and shields. But Slow, armed with only a coup stick, takes off ahead of the others. As one of the Crow warriors is about to shoot an arrow, Slow hits his arm with his coup stick, causing the warrior to miss his target. When the Crow see the other Sioux warriors coming, they flee. None of the Hunkpapa have been hurt. Slow is a hero.

Slow's father is so proud that he gives the boy a new name, the first name the buffalo bull spoke to him. This name means "Sitting Bull." Sitting Bull grew up to become one of the greatest Lakota warriors in history.

Pioneer Girl

Pioneer Girl is the true story of Grace McCance and her family. In 1885, the McCance family filed a claim on land in Nebraska. They moved from Missouri to the shortgrass prairie and became homesteaders.

Homesteaders had to watch the weather carefully. Hailstorms could destroy crops. Lightning could spark a fire if the weather was dry. Grace never forgot the first prairie fire that she saw as a child. Luckily, it died down right before it reached their house. A few months later, a rainstorm hit their homestead. Their sod house shook; the roof was torn off. Everything on the walls and shelves was either smashed or blown away.

But there were also good memories. Before their first Christmas on the prairie, the McCances received three barrels full of molasses, apples, walnuts, and clothes from Grace's grandparents in Missouri.

Most of the McCance's neighbors were European immigrants. Many came to farm the land, but some also came for religious freedom or to avoid paying high taxes. Most were poor. Everyone in the family had to work six days a week, including children as young as three and four.

At age five, Grace herded the family's cows. She drove them to the fields each morning, stayed with them during the day, and brought them home at night. One young cow had an especially bad temper. She charged Grace one day and left her with a bad cut. Grace's father sold the cow a few days later and Grace kept herding. Life on the prairie was never easy.

Black Cowboy, Wild Horses

Black Cowboy, Wild Horses is about the African American cowboy, Bob Lemmons. With the help of his stallion, Warrior, Lemmons herds mustangs, the wild horses that live on the plains. He herds them by making the mustangs think that he is one of them.

The selection shows Lemmons on the job. First, he looks for the herd's hoof marks. Then he rides Warrior and catches up to them as a storm breaks. It is important that he doesn't get too close too soon. If the mustangs see or smell him, they will run off. He moves Warrior very slowly, trying not to make a sound, getting closer as the herd grazes. The stallion leading the herd looks around before he goes back to grazing. The mustangs sense that Lemmons is near, but they think that he is a horse.

Lemmons rides into the middle of the herd. He tries to keep himself flat across Warrior's back. The next day, a colt is bitten by a rattlesnake and dies. As the stallion moves the herd away, Lemmons decides that this is the right moment to take over the herd. He and Warrior gallop to the front. Warrior rears up and kicks his legs into the air. Then he charges the stallion. Warrior and the stallion fight, kicking at each other. Warrior wins the battle, and the mustang stallion leaves the herd.

Lemmons is now in charge of the mustangs. As he rides back home, the herd follows him. After a two-day ride, he leads the mustangs straight into the corral. The other cowboys take over the job and Lemmons rides off with Warrior.

Elena

Elena takes place in Mexico in 1910, at the beginning of
the Mexican Revolution. Elena's husband, Pablo, a sombrero
maker, has to leave town on business. Elena is worried for his
safety. Armed soldiers are everywhere. The rainy season has
just ended, and the road is not in good condition. Sure enough,
there is a landslide, and Pablo and his horse fall into a ravine.
Villagers lift him to safety, but he is badly injured. Before he
dies, he tells Elena that she and their four children must leave
the village to be safe.

The army of Pancho Villa arrives in their village. Villa is
fighting to free Mexico from a cruel dictator. But Villa is a former
bandit who does not respect the law. Elena hides her son,
Esteban, in a kitchen cabinet, afraid that Villa will force him into
his army. She brings their horses into the kitchen, too, so they
won't be stolen.

Villa himself knocks on the door. When he finds out that
Pablo has died, he asks if there are any sombreros left. Elena
sells him the last one. She knows that it is time for her family
to leave.

Elena and her family leave all their belongings behind.
They board a train and travel north to the city of Juárez on the
United States border. They are able to cross into the United
States and end up settling in Santa Ana, California, because it
reminds them of their home.

Years later, the family finds out that their old village was
burned by soldiers. Only then do they realize how Elena's
courage saved them all.

The Grizzly Bear Family Book

The Grizzly Bear Family Book is a nonfiction selection about grizzly bears in the Alaskan wilderness, especially in Denali National Park. The author and photographer, Michio Hoshino, spent a year in Alaska observing grizzly bears.

The selection begins in winter, during which grizzlies are asleep in their dens and mother bears give birth to their cubs. In the spring, the bears wake up and leave their dens. Grizzlies are thinner at this time because they haven't eaten in months. As the weather gets warmer, the bears eat roots, grasses, ground squirrels, and other animals.

During the summer, grizzlies fish in rivers and streams. They are skilled at catching fish and especially like salmon. Although they usually prefer being alone, bears come together when fishing. The stronger, or dominant, bears get the best fishing spots. Mothers bring their young cubs food. When the cubs turn two, they can fish by themselves. They learn how to catch fish by watching their mothers.

In the fall, the grizzlies start eating enough food to get them through the winter. They fill up on berries, which are high in sugar. Sometimes, bears eat berries for twenty hours a day! They hardly stop to sleep.

Then the daylight hours grow short and winter arrives again. The grizzly bears return to their dens and settle in for another long winter's sleep.

The Golden Lion Tamarin Comes Home

The nonfiction selection *The Golden Lion Tamarin Comes Home* is about the work people are doing to bring a kind of monkey called a golden lion tamarin back to its natural habitat, the coastal Brazilian rain forest. The rain forest was once 1500 miles long, but most of the trees have been cut down or burned to clear the land. Only a small part of the rain forest remains. As the forest disappeared, so did the tamarins. The Golden Lion Tamarin Conservation Program was begun to help bring the tamarins back into the wild.

Today zoos around the world breed tamarins. But zoo tamarins do not know how to hunt for food or how to survive in the wild. One zoo in Washington, D.C., has been trying to prepare tamarins to live in the wild. Then the zoo sends the tamarins to the Brazilian rain forest.

The tamarins are flown to Brazil and taken to a reserve. First, they are put into cages in trees to get used to the sights and sounds of the forest. Then, when they are ready, they are set free. Observers watch the tamarins closely to see how they are doing. Some of the tamarins wear radio collars so observers can keep track of them.

Tamarins need the most help just after they are released from the cages. They can get lost or injured very easily. The observers give them plenty of food and water at first. When the tamarins become more independent and know their way around, the feedings stop. Unfortunately, only about thirty percent of these tamarins survive for more than two years in the wild. The goal of the conservation program is to make that number grow.

My Side of the Mountain

My Side of the Mountain tells the story of Sam Gribley, who has decided to live in the woods with only his diary and a few animals for company. These include Frightful, the falcon that Sam has raised from a chick; a weasel that he calls The Baron; and Jessie C. James, a raccoon.

It is September. Sam notices that The Baron Weasel's fur is turning white. He knows that winter will arrive soon. It will be cold and food will be hard to find. He makes some fur clothes to keep himself warm. He decides to build a clay fireplace to heat the hollowed-out tree he lives in. It takes days to get the fireplace to work right.

By October, Sam begins to look for ripe walnuts and hickory nuts to store for the winter. He needs to gather them quickly because the squirrels are also after them. Soon he has a store-house filled with nuts. Next, he competes with the squirrels, raccoons, and a skunk for apples. The animals are fattening themselves up before their winter sleep.

On Halloween night, Sam throws a party for his animal neighbors. The squirrels, foxes, raccoons, and opossums come for their treats of nuts, rabbit meat, apples, and crayfish. Sam has always been careful about not leaving food out. On this night, however, he forgets to protect the food that he has been storing in his house. Sleeping outside, Sam wakes up to noises in his tree. The animals have found all his food! Now that he has invited all of the animals over, he doesn't know how to make them go away. He finally snarls and makes loud noises to frighten them. His guests leave. Halloween is over.

Reading Cards

Reading Routines

Before You Read . . .

Page through the selection. Read the headings and look at the pictures to get an idea of what the selection is about.

As You Read . . .

- **Fill in your Event Map.** Finish each sentence to tell the order in which events occurred.

- **Think of questions** or comments to discuss with your classmates after reading the selection.

Theme 1: Nature's Fury

Literature Discussion

Discuss your own questions and the following questions with a group of your classmates:

- How does the story remind you of any real-life experiences?

- How is Jonathan protective of Abby?

- What would you like to ask Jonathan about his experience? What would you like to ask Abby?

Theme 1: Nature's Fury

The Way I See It

Character's Perspective

This story is told from Jonathan's perspective. The reader experiences the same sounds, smells, memories, and sensations as Jonathan. How would the story be different if it were told from the perspective of Abby or Moose?

- For Abby, consider her age, her physical limitations, and her feelings toward her brother.

- For Moose, consider his extrasensitive senses of smell and hearing, and his inability to speak to Abby and Jonathan.

Theme 1: Nature's Fury

Create a Different Picture

Similes

Sometimes, in order to describe an object, person, or event, an author compares it to something else, using words such as *like* or *as*. This comparison is called a simile. For example, the simile "the ground swelled and retreated, like ocean waves" creates a vivid picture of the earth's movements.

- Find other instances in the story where the author has used similes.

- Choose one of the similes, and change it. For example, what picture is created if "the ground swelled and retreated" like ripples on a pond?

Theme 1: Nature's Fury

Reading Routines

Before You Read . . .

Page through the selection. Read the headings and look at the photographs to get an idea of what the selection is about.

As You Read . . .

- **Write down the questions** you came up with and any other comments you have about the selection.

- **Fill in your Selection Map.** Write a sentence telling what each section is about.

Theme 1: Nature's Fury

Literature Discussion

Discuss your own questions and the following questions with a group of your classmates:

- What traits and skills does a storm chaser need? Does Warren Faidley seem to have these? Give examples that support your answer.

- Why do you think people were so amazed by Warren's photo of the lightning bolt hitting the pole?

- Do you think this photo was worth the risks Warren took to get it? Why or why not?

- How do you think Warren felt when he realized that there was a strong demand for storm photos? Why might he have felt that way?

Theme 1: Nature's Fury

Picture This!

Descriptive Language

The author uses descriptive language to tell the readers about lightning and tornadoes. For example, he refers to a "jagged bolt" of lightning. Locate these terms in the selection, and use them to create your own descriptions.

Warren's Eventful Day

Organize Information Visually

How could you summarize the events of May 5, 1993? Create a graphic organizer, such as a schedule or a logbook entry with sketches, that gives an at-a-glance view of that day's events.

May 5, 1993 Amarillo, Texas	6:00 AM:	Awake in motel room in Tornado Alley; check weather on TV
	12:15 PM:	Arrive at National Weather Service; get update on conditions
	2:00 PM:	Final chase decisions made

It Looks Like. . .

Comparing by Shape

The author compares the shapes of the tornadoes to various objects, including an elephant's trunk, an anvil, a wedge, and a funnel. Make a list of all the shapes the author uses. Next to each shape name, draw what that type of tornado might look like.

Theme 1: Nature's Fury

Reading Routines

Before You Read . . .

Preview the selection. Read the first page. Then look at all the photographs in the selection.

As You Read . . .

- **Monitor your understanding.** If you come to a part you don't understand, pause for a moment. Reread or look at the photos to clarify.

- **Think of questions** to discuss with your classmates when you finish reading.

- **Fill in your Category Map** to help you understand what causes volcanoes of various kinds.

Theme 1: Nature's Fury

Literature Discussion

Discuss your own questions and the following questions with a group of your classmates:

- On page 85, the author describes two ways in which ancient peoples explained volcanoes. What is another explanation ancient peoples might have given for them?

- What kinds of things do you think visitors to the Mount St. Helens National Monument might see? How might this view change over time?

- The earth's crust is made up of many huge plates. Why is this knowledge useful to people who try to predict and map volcanic eruptions?

Theme 1: Nature's Fury

Volcanic History

Make a Time Line

Use the information about Mount St. Helens the author gives, as well as the photos of the mountain, to create an illustrated time line showing Mount St. Helens's recent volcanic history. Begin the time line in the mid-1800s, and end it in the present.

**Mid–
1800s**

Today

Theme 1: Nature's Fury

Take Another Look

Comparisons

On page 96, the author compares a plugged-up dome volcano to a bottle of soda water with a cork in it. Find some other comparisons the author has used to help readers understand volcanoes. Look on pages 88, 89, and 94. Then make up a new comparison in place of each one the author has used. Try to make your comparison as vivid as you can.

Theme 1: Nature's Fury

Reading Routines

Before You Read . . .

Read the introduction. Think about the challenges a young skater might face.

As You Read . . .

- **Make judgments** as you read. Ask yourself whether you're getting to know Michelle Kwan. Also **evaluate** whether the information you are reading is presenting facts or opinions.

- **Think of questions** you would like to discuss with your classmates after you finish reading.

- Fill in your **Fact and Opinion Chart**.

Theme 2: Give It All You've Got

Literature Discussion

Discuss your own questions and the following questions with a group of your classmates:

- What do you think Michelle Kwan was like when she was twelve? How do you think she might have changed by the time she wrote the autobiography?

- Why do you think Michelle mentions not-so-attractive details such as skaters' ugly feet? Does this make you like Michelle more or less? Why?

- What qualities of Michelle's do you think made her a successful skater? Do you admire these qualities? Why or why not?

Theme 2: Give It All You've Got

We Need To Talk

Create a Dialogue

Write the conversation that might have taken place between Michelle and her coach Frank Carroll in this scene: Michelle has just arrived at the ice rink for her first lesson with Frank. Frank has just returned from the Canadian Conference and she has returned from passing the Senior test in Los Angeles. Now Michelle has to tell Frank that she can no longer skate at the lower levels. If you need help getting started, here are a few opening lines you might use:

- "Hi, Frank," Michelle said timidly. "How was Canada?"

- "Good morning, Michelle," said Frank. "Let's get to work. We need to get you ready for the Junior Nationals competition next year."

Theme 2: Give It All You've Got

Funny Figure

Make a Humorous Diagram

Michelle tells readers many details about figure skating. Some are fascinating, and others are not very glamorous. Make a cartoon-style drawing of a skater. Label the skater's

- brain (page 148)
- nose (page 149)
- gloves (page 149)
- feet (page 149)

- fancy costume (pages 149 and 152)
- boots (page 150)
- skate blades (page 150)

Write a funny or interesting caption to go with each label. The page numbers shown above will tell you where to look for information you can use in your captions.

Theme 2: Give It All You've Got

Reading Routines

Before You Read . . .

Preview the story. Read the title and first paragraph. Then look at the pictures.

As You Read . . .

- **Think of questions** to discuss with your classmates after you read the selection.

- **Sum up** the most important events.

- Write the main events in your **Story Map**.

Theme 2: Give It All You've Got

Literature Discussion

Discuss your own questions and the following questions with a group of your classmates:

- What kind of person would you say Manuel is? What details show his personality and character?

- Do you think Mr. Roybal is a good person to be in charge of the talent show? Why or why not?

- Why do you think Manuel doesn't tell his family what he will be doing in the talent show?

- Do you think Manuel is right to be so confident that things will go well? How do you think you would feel in his position?

Theme 2: Give It All You've Got

On A Funny Note

Humor

Gary Soto is well-known for including humor in his stories. As you read, note passages that are funny. For example, in the second paragraph on page 166, the author gives a funny description of Manuel as he shows Benny what he plans to do in the talent show. Think about what makes the passages funny. You might compare the passages you find with the ones another student has found. Discuss which passages you like best, and why.

Theme 2: Give It All You've Got

Are They Real?

Details That Add Realism

Authors of realistic fiction often include details that make characters and events seem realistic. As you read, make a list of details that make Manuel seem like a real boy, Mr. Roybal seem like a real adult, and Manuel's family seem like a real family.

Theme 2: Give It All You've Got

Reading Routines

Before You Read . . .

Page through the selection. Look at the illustrations.

As You Read . . .

- **Make inferences** based on details from the story and your own knowledge.

- Use details from the story along with personal experiences to **predict** what might happen next.

- **Think of questions** you would like to discuss with your classmates after reading the selection.

- **Fill in your Predictions Chart**.

Theme 2: Give It All You've Got

Literature Discussion

Discuss your own questions and the following questions with a group of your classmates:

- Do you think the author has done a good job of creating a suspenseful situation? Why or why not?

- Have you ever felt like you had a drum beating in your chest? Describe what was happening.

- Do you think Doug is brave? Why or why not?

- Which of the animals that Doug has seen is the most interesting to you? Explain why.

- What do you think Doug will do when he finally reaches the Fear Place?

Theme 2: Give It All You've Got

Words That Rock

Descriptive Language

The setting of *The Fear Place* is a very important element in the story. Think about the words and phrases the author uses to help you picture the place where Doug is hiking.

- Make a list of the words and phrases that describe the time of day and the rocks, mountains, cliffs, and other things Doug sees, hears, and feels as he follows the path.

- Picture in your mind what the setting is like, and write a paragraph that describes the setting for someone who has never been there before.

Compare your description to one written by a classmate.

Theme 2: Give It All You've Got

Look At It This Way

Figurative Language

Authors use comparisons to help readers imagine how something looks, sounds, smells, tastes or feels. The author of *The Fear Place* uses the following comparison to describe the movements of Charlie the cougar:

> *It seemed to Doug that her long body must be moving backward in sections, like a caterpillar.* (page 200)

This is an example of *simile*. A simile is a comparison of two things using the word *like* or *as*. Look through the story to find two other examples of similes. Write down the page number, and the two things the author is comparing in each simile you find.

Theme 2: Give It All You've Got

Reading Card 13 — Mae Jemison: Space Scientist

Reading Routines

Before You Read . . .

Preview the selection. Read the title, look at the photographs, and read the captions. Try to figure out what the topic of the selection is.

As You Read . . .

- **Think of questions** to discuss with your classmates after you read the selection.

- Look for the **main ideas**.

- Write the main ideas in your **Main Ideas Chart**.

Reading Card 14 — Mae Jemison: Space Scientist

Literature Discussion

Discuss your own questions and the following questions with a group of your classmates:

- What did Mae Jemison do as a teenager and a young adult to try to make her dream come true?

- Do you think Mae Jemison would have succeeded at anything she tried? Why or why not?

- What are some other careers Mae Jemison might have pursued? Use information from the selection to support your answer.

- What impresses you most about Mae Jemison so far?

Time and Space

Tense Shifts

Reread the third paragraph on page 219. Note how the author shifts from the past tense in the first two sentences to the present tense in the third sentence. (The verbs *got* and *flew* are in the past tense; the verbs *climbs* and *loops* are in the present tense.) Find other examples of a shift in tense in the selection. Then discuss with a classmate why you think the author has included these shifts.

Theme 2: Give It All You've Got

One Step At a Time

Outlining

Use the information on pages 216–221 of the selection to make an outline showing how people train to become an astronaut and what the work of a mission specialist is like. You might want to consult an encyclopedia or a trade book about astronauts to find more information to include in your outline.

The beginning of your outline might look like this:

I. An astronaut's training
   A.   physical training
      1
      2
   B.   survival training

Theme 2: Give It All You've Got

Reading Routines

Before You Read . . .

Page through the selection. Look at the illustrations.

As You Read . . .

- **Evaluate** how successful the author is in telling the story. Use details from the selection and your experience to make your evaluations.

- Think about the **author's viewpoint**. Does the author feel positively or negatively toward the subject?

- **Fill in your Author's Viewpoint Chart**.

- **Think of questions** to discuss with your classmates when you are finished reading.

Theme 3: Voices of the Revolution

Literature Discussion

Discuss your own questions and the following questions with a group of your classmates:

- Which of Paul Revere's jobs do you think is the most interesting? Explain why.

- Do you think you would have enjoyed living in Boston during Paul Revere's lifetime? Why?

- Do you think the Sons of Liberty were right to dump the tea in Boston Harbor? Why or why not?

- What do you think it would have been like to be one of Paul Revere's children?

Theme 3: Voices of the Revolution

Let Me Tell It My Way

Point of View

And Then What Happened, Paul Revere? is written from the third-person point of view with a narrator telling the events of Paul Revere's life. Work with a partner to choose a favorite scene from the story and rewrite it from Paul Revere's point of view.

- Make a list of the main events in your scene.

- Think about what it would have been like to be Paul Revere living through the events.

Write an account of what happened. Remember to use the words *I*, *me*, and *my* to refer to what Paul Revere says and does.

Theme 3: Voices of the Revolution

Occupations

Specialized Vocabulary

In *And Then What Happened, Paul Revere?* you learn about the many jobs Paul Revere had during his lifetime. Go back through the story and make a list of all his jobs. Next to each occupation, brainstorm several words that describe the skills required to do the job well. Compare your list to those of your classmates. Together, talk about Paul Revere's many talents.

Theme 3: Voices of the Revolution

Reading Routines

Before You Read . . .

Read the first few paragraphs of the story. Look at the illustrations. Try to get a sense of **where** and **when** the story takes place.

As You Read . . .

- **Pause** from time to time. **Sum up** the most important story events.

- **Think about** why the characters act as they do.

- Fill in your **Cause and Effect Chart**.

- **Think of questions** to discuss with your classmates after reading the selection.

Theme 3: Voices of the Revolution

Literature Discussion

Discuss your own questions and the following questions with a group of your classmates:

- What do you think Katie finds most difficult about the conflict she is experiencing? Give details from the story that support your answer.

- What kind of person is Katie? Think of five adjectives that describe her. Name a story detail or event that reveals each trait.

- *Katie's Trunk* is an example of historical fiction, a made-up story based on events that really happened. Do you think the author has done a good job of giving readers a feeling for what life was like in the past? Why or why not?

- What do you think will happen to Katie next? Why?

Theme 3: Voices of the Revolution

The Way They Feel

Figurative Language

The author of this story has included many examples of figurative language to help give readers a strong sense of how the characters feel. Find these examples on page 294:

- "It makes me skittish as a newborn calf" is an example of a **simile**. A simile compares two unlike things using the words *like* or *as*. Here, the author is comparing a nervous and jittery calf with the way Mama feels.

- Find other examples of similes as you read. You can locate them on these pages: 296, 297, 298, 300, 301, 302, and 303.

Theme 3: Voices of the Revolution

It Was Like This . . .

Point of View

This story is told from Katie's point of view. What if it had been told from another point of view? With a classmate, discuss how each of the following scenes might have been described differently if one of the following characters had told about it.

SCENES	CHARACTERS
• the rebels approaching the house	• Walter
• the rebels smashing things inside the house	• Mama
• John Warren discovering Katie in the trunk	• John Warren

Theme 3: Voices of the Revolution

Reading Card 9　James Forten

Reading Routines

Before You Read . . .

Page through the selection. Look at the illustrations to get an idea of what the story is about.

As You Read . . .

- **Think of questions** that can be answered as you read or after you read. Look for answers to your questions.

- **Fill in the third column of your K-W-L Chart**. You may also wish to add new questions to the second column as you read, as well as answers to these questions in the third column.

Theme 3: Voices of the Revolution

Reading Card 10　James Forten

Literature Discussion

Discuss your own questions and the following questions with a group of your classmates:

- Do you think you would have liked living in colonial Philadelphia? Why or why not?

- Why do you think both of James Forten's parents believed strongly that he should get an education? Do you agree with their opinion? Explain your answer.

- Why were *privateers* useful during America's war for independence? Do you think it was a good decision for the colonies to use private ships to help fight the war? Why or why not?

Theme 3: Voices of the Revolution

Setting the Mood

Descriptive Language

List the adjectives and other descriptive words the author uses to show what early morning was like in colonial Philadelphia. For example, the author describes how the "windows in the city were coming alive with the glow of lamplight." Discuss with your classmates how the author uses these words to help the reader visualize the setting.

Theme 3: Voices of the Revolution

On Schedule

Organize Information Visually

Reread pages 322–323. Summarize the events of October 16th, 1781 using a graphic organizer such as a captain's log entry. In your summary, you should briefly mention each important event in the order it happened. You might use sketches or diagrams to illustrate each event.

16th October, 1781	The *Royal Louis* and its crew surrenders to the British.

Theme 3: Voices of the Revolution

The Way He Sees It

Character's Perspective

Reread the description of the prison ship the *Jersey* on page 325. Note that it is written from the third-person point of view. Now rewrite the scene from James Forten's perspective, as if he were describing it on his first day there. Before you write, work with a few classmates to answer the following questions:

- What do you think James felt and thought when he saw the *Jersey* from a distance? When he first stepped on board the ship and saw the conditions for the prisoners there?

- How do you think James interacted with the white prisoners on board the *Jersey*?

Theme 3: Voices of the Revolution

Reading Routines

Before You Read . . .

Preview the story. Read the introduction. Look at the pictures. Think about what Mariah needs to do to plan and organize a surprise party for her sister Lynn.

As You Read . . .

- **Fill in your Problem-Solution Chart.** Complete each sentence under the heading **Solution.**

- **Think of questions** to discuss with your classmates when you are finished reading.

- **Make inferences** about story characters using information in the story and your personal knowledge.

Theme 4: Person to Person

Literature Discussion

Discuss your own questions and the following questions with a group of your classmates:

- Have you ever helped make a surprise party for someone? Explain what happened.

- How do you think you would react to the problems Mariah is having with her sister?

- Is it wrong for Mariah and her friends to mislead Lynn about what they are doing at Brandon's house? Why or why not?

- What do you think about Lynn's desire to stay in bed all day on her birthday? Explain your opinion.

Theme 4: Person to Person

Just Do It This Way

Directions

Look at the illustration on page 351. Reread the last paragraph on the page. Then use clues from the story and the illustration along with your own knowledge to write directions for how to make paper flowers. Before you write

- make a list of the material you will need and

- figure out the different steps and put them in order

Write the directions on a separate sheet of paper. You may want to use a numbered list or write signal words such as *first*, *next*, and *then* to show the order of steps. You also may want to include small drawings to go with some of the steps.

Theme 4: Person to Person

My Party and Her Party

Compare and Contrast

Compare Lynn's party to a birthday party you've been to that you really enjoyed. Make two lists that include details about each party. Where did the party take place? What were the decorations like? Who came to the party? Were there any special activities or gifts? If so, what were they?

On another sheet of paper, create a Venn diagram like the one below to compare the two parties. Use the details from your lists to help you show how the parties are alike and how they are different.

Your Party   Both   Lynn's Party

Theme 4: Person to Person

Reading Routines

Before You Read . . .

Page through the selection. Look at the photographs.

As You Read . . .

- **Monitor your understanding** by pausing periodically and asking yourself questions about what you have read.

- **Clarify ideas you don't understand** by rereading, reading ahead, looking at pictures, or asking questions.

- **Fill in your Details Chart**.

- **Think of questions** to discuss with your classmates after reading the selection.

Theme 4: Person to Person

Literature Discussion

Discuss your own questions and the following questions with a group of your classmates:

- Have you ever had a pet you were very attached to? Describe the animal and tell why you felt (or feel) the way you do.

- Do you think the narrator will grow to love her mother's new dog guide as much as she loved Marit? Why or why not?

- What activities do you enjoy that might be difficult to do if you lost your sight? What adaptations might you make that would enable you to continue doing these activities? How could a dog guide help?

Theme 4: Person to Person

Let Me Tell You About My Day

Write a Diary Entry

Reread page 374. Pay attention to the details the narrator gives about Mom's first day at Seeing Eye. Then write an account of that day from the first-person point of view.

- Include details about what the narrator did, saw, and felt.

- Remember that, since you are using the first-person point of view, you should use words such as *I, me,* and *my*.

When you are finished, exchange your passage with a partner. Discuss the similarities and differences.

Theme 4: Person to Person

Working As a Team

Summarize Information Graphically

Mom's first several days at Seeing Eye are extremely busy. She and Ursula go on two walks a day, learning new routes and adjusting to each other. Slowly they learn to work together as a team. Summarize their progress by creating a flowchart that shows the steps they take in the correct order. You can add to your flowchart as you continue reading the story.

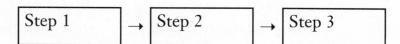

Step 1 → Step 2 → Step 3

Theme 4: Person to Person

Mixed Emotions

Mind Map

The characters in a selection often face some sort of problem or conflict. This struggle can be external (such as fighting an enemy) or internal (such as overcoming a fear). In this nonfiction piece, the narrator describes her inner conflict when her mother gets a new dog guide. Create a Mind Map with two columns to describe her mixed feelings. List the reasons she worries about her mother getting a new dog on the left column, under "Fears." Then list the reasons she feels hopeful and positive about these same things on the right side, under "Hopes."

Mind Map	
Fears	**Hopes**

Theme 4: Person to Person

Reading Routines

Before You Read . . .

Preview the story. Read the introduction. Look at the pictures. Think about what this story might be about.

As You Read . . .

- **Think of questions** to discuss with your classmates after you read.

- **Fill in your Venn Diagram**. Identify story details showing what Second Sister and Yingtao (Fourth Brother) are like. Place the details in the appropriate parts of the diagram to show how the brother and sister are similar and how they are different.

Theme 4: Person to Person

Literature Discussion

Discuss your own questions and the following questions with a group of your classmates:

- Yingtao (Fourth Brother) is not sure about playing a trick on his sister. What does this tell you about him?

- Based on details from the story and your own experiences, do you think Second Sister's attitude towards Paul Eng is fair? Explain.

- What is the goal of Third Sister and Fourth Brother's plan? Do you think the plan will achieve that goal? Explain your opinion.

- Do you agree with Third Brother that he and Third Sister said enough to trick Second Sister? Why or why not?

Theme 4: Person to Person

This Is My Friend Yingtao

Character Development

Authors reveal what their story characters are like through the things the characters say and do. Look back through the story at the words and actions of Fourth Brother, Yingtao. You may want to think about the following details:

- Yingtao remembers times when Second Sister was kind to him.

- He lets his friend Matthew take his place in the string quartet.

- He asks, "Can you hog a dish of pork?"

- He defends Paul when Second Sister criticizes him.

Now create a character sketch of Yingtao. Begin by telling what kind of a person he is. Then use the details you've noted to defend your view.

Theme 4: Person to Person

Let Me Tell It My Way

Dialogue

Second Sister and Fourth Brother stage two conversations to trick Second Sister and Paul Eng into believing that they like each other. Look back at the exact words spoken by the characters in each conversation. (Remember that Kim O'Meara is part of the second conversation.) Think about how the characters might have made their words more convincing. Then write a new script for each conversation.

After you have finished your script, exchange it with a partner. Make suggestions for how to make the language sound more natural. Use the suggestions to revise your script.

Theme 4: Person to Person

Reading Routines

Before You Read . . .

Page through the selection. Look at the illustrations.

As You Read . . .

- **Evaluate** how successful the author is in telling the story. Use story details and your own experience to help you make your evaluations.

- **Fill in your Inferences Chart**.

- **Think of questions** to discuss with your classmates when you are finished reading.

Theme 4: Person to Person

Literature Discussion

Discuss your own questions and the following questions with a group of your classmates:

- Based on his diary entries, what is your opinion of Leigh Botts's writing?

- Do you think Leigh is likely to become a professional writer someday? Why or why not?

- Why do you think the author decided to write this story as a series of diary entries instead of in regular paragraph form? Do you think it is a good way for an author to tell a story? Why or why not?

Theme 4: Person to Person

To Write or Not to Write

List the Reasons

Leigh Botts almost did not enter the Young Writers' writing contest. As things turned out, he probably was very glad he decided to enter it! Work with some classmates to develop a list of reasons why entering such contests is a good idea. Afterward, share your list with the class.

Theme 4: Person to Person

Angela Badger's Advice for Aspiring Writers

Create a Poster

When Angela Badger talks with Leigh about his writing, she says what she thinks young writers should try to do—and *not* try to do. Reread page 454 in *Dear Mr. Henshaw*. Use what Mrs. Badger says there to create a poster entitled "Angela Badger's Advice for Aspiring Writers."

Theme 4: Person to Person

Reading Routines

Before You Read . . .

Read the title and look at the illustrations. Also read the first page of the story.

As You Read . . .

- Use story information and your own knowledge to **make inferences** about the story characters and events.

- Use story clues to draw conclusions about characters and events. **Fill in your Conclusions Chart**.

- **Think of questions** to discuss with your classmates after reading the selection.

Theme 5: One Land, Many Trails

Literature Discussion

Discuss your own questions and the following questions with a group of your classmates:

- What is your opinion of the naming custom followed by the Lakota Sioux?

- Do you think such a custom would work in the modern world? Why or why not?

- How would you describe Slow at the age of seven? Ten? Fourteen?

- Think about the four new names Returns Again was given by the buffalo. What importance do you think these names will have as the story continues to unfold?

Theme 5: One Land, Many Trails

Hunkpapa Glossary

Language Study

The author has included several words and phrases from the Hunkpapa language. List as many of these words and phrases as you can find. Use clues in the other words and sentences to write the meaning of each one. Then create an alphabetized glossary of Hunkpapa terms.

Note: You'll be able to figure out the meaning of only one of the four names the buffalo bull gives Returns Again, but you can figure out which Hunkpapa word means "bull."

Theme 5: One Land, Many Trails

Facts or Imagination?

Noting Details

The author of *A Boy Called Slow* based his story on the life of a real person, but he also made up some details. For example, he probably invented the lines of dialogue characters say to each other. He might also have invented details such as Slow pulling a burr from his horse's mane. Make a list of details you think the author of this story made up. Make another list of details that are probably facts, such as the name of the Plains Indians group Slow was a part of. Record your details in a chart.

Details the Author Made Up	Details That Are Facts

Theme 5: One Land, Many Trails

Reading Card 5   Pioneer Girl

Reading Routines

Before You Read . . .

Page through the selection. Look at the photographs to get an idea of what pioneer life on the Great Plains was like.

As You Read . . .

- **Think of questions** to discuss with your classmates when you are finished reading.

- **Complete your K-W-L Chart.** Write down things you already know about pioneer life, things you'd like to learn, and information you gain from reading the selection.

Theme 5: One Land, Many Trails

Reading Card 6   Pioneer Girl

Literature Discussion

Discuss your own questions and the following questions with a group of your classmates:

- What hardships does the author describe?

- What happy times does she describe? Do the hard times and happy times seem to balance out? Explain.

- In your opinion, does the author do a good job of helping you understand what life was like for children living on the prairie? If so, how does she do this?

- Based on what you've learned so far, do you think you'd have enjoyed life on a pioneer farm? Why or why not?

Theme 5: One Land, Many Trails

Visit Our Past

Plan a Pioneer Museum Display

The pioneer era is an important part of our nation's history. What could a museum put on display that would give visitors a sense of what life was like for the pioneers on the Great Plains? Work with some classmates to develop a plan for such a display. Prepare a sketch of how you would arrange your display in the museum. You might choose to include some of these things:

- vehicles
- tools
- clothing
- things used for recreation
- photographs
- films or live demonstrations of how things were done

Theme 5: One Land, Many Trails

On Stage

Act Out a Scene

Work with some classmates. Choose a scene in *Pioneer Girl* to dramatize.

- Select a scene that involves at least three characters.

- Rewrite the dialogue in script form. Include stage directions. Add additional dialogue that will make the scene more interesting.

- Add events that might have happened before or after the one you've chosen. Write dialogue for those events. Include stage directions.

- Assign parts to group members. Rehearse the scene. Then present your scene in front of the class.

Theme 5: One Land, Many Trails

Reading Routines

Before You Read . . .

Preview the selection. Read the title. Look at the illustrations.

As You Read . . .

- **Think of questions** to discuss with your classmates when you are finished reading.

- Look for opportunities to **make judgments** about characters' actions.

- List the judgments you make on your **Judgments Chart**.

Theme 5: One Land, Many Trails

Literature Discussion

Discuss your own questions and the following questions with a group of your classmates:

- What has Bob Lemmons accomplished so far?

- What does he still need to do to bring in the herd?

- Do you think there are any similarities between Bob Lemmon's life as a cowboy and the lives of cowboys today? If so, what are they?

- Why do you think people today are interested in reading about old-time cowboys such as Bob Lemmons?

Theme 5: One Land, Many Trails

Mustang Catchers Wanted

A How-to Guide

Bob Lemmons has begun the process of bringing in a herd of mustangs, something very few people have ever been able to do without a great deal of help. As you read, make a list of the things Bob does to accomplish this task. Then use your list to write a how-to guide for cowboys who want to become successful mustang catchers.

Theme 5: One Land, Many Trails

Read Between The Lines

Subtle Meanings

Look at these phrases from page 529 of the story:

- *as hard and stinging as remorse*

- *as white as grief*

The words *remorse* and *grief* are used in colorful phrases that help describe the rain and the moon. The author uses these words for that purpose. He may also want these words to have a second, more subtle meaning, though. Think about these two words. Might they suggest something about Bob Lemmons's life that the author does not explain in the story but wants readers to think about on their own? Discuss this question with a partner or a small group.

Theme 5: One Land, Many Trails

Reading Routines

Before You Read . . .

Preview the story. Read the introduction on page 551. Look at the pictures.

As You Read . . .

- **Summarize the story**. After you have read a few pages, pause to summarize in your own words the events you have just read about. Include only the most important details in your summary.

- **Fill in your Story Map**. Be sure to include only the most important story events in the **Plot** section of your chart.

- **Think of questions** to discuss with your classmates when you are finished reading.

Theme 5: One Land, Many Trails

Literature Discussion

Discuss your own questions and the following questions with a group of your classmates:

- How would you describe Pablo and Elena's marriage? Give examples from the story to support your answer.

- Describing the beautiful days after her father's death, the narrator says, "It was as if nature were mocking us." What does she mean by this?

- How does the visit from Pancho Villa help Elena?

- The narrator says that Elena understood that everything that had happened to her before had been for a reason. What does she mean by this?

Theme 5: One Land, Many Trails

Remembering the Details

Character Development

Authors reveal what their characters are like in a number of different ways:

- through the characters' actions

- through the characters' words

- through what other characters say about them

As you read *Elena*, think about how the author portrays the main character. Keep a list of the things that Elena says and does, as well as her daughter Rosa's comments about her. Then write a paragraph in which you tell what Elena was like.

Theme 5: One Land, Many Trails

When We Moved to California . . .

Figurative Language

Reread the paragraphs in which the following statements are made.

- *It was as if nature were mocking us*. (last paragraph on page 552) In this sentence nature is said to act as a human might. This is called *personification*.

- *Looking down, I saw our street transformed into a river of sombreros*. (first paragraph on page 554) In this sentence the appearance of Pancho Villa's army is compared to a river. This is called *metaphor*.

Now think about the family's experiences on their trip to California and once they settle in Santa Ana. Choose a scene from this part of the story and write a paragraph describing it. Include several figures of speech in your description.

Theme 5: One Land, Many Trails

Reading Routines

Before You Read . . .

Read the title and look at the photographs.

As You Read . . .

- **Look for general statements** the author makes about bears, about people, and about the wilderness. Write the generalizations you find in your **Generalizations Chart**.

- **Evaluate** how well the author tells his story. Think about how his personal involvement with his subject enhances his descriptions.

- **Think of questions** to discuss with your classmates when you are finished reading.

Theme 6: Animal Encounters

Literature Discussion

Discuss your own questions and the following questions with a group of your classmates:

- How does the author seem to feel about grizzly bears and the Alaskan wilderness? Find specific passages that support your answer.

- The author has organized the selection carefully. He starts by describing the bears in early spring, and goes on to describe their behavior throughout the other seasons. Do you think this is a good way to organize the selection? Explain.

- Do you think you would enjoy photographing grizzly bears in the Alaskan wilderness? Why or why not?

Theme 6: Animal Encounters

Grizzly Bear Calendar

Noting Details

Use facts from the selection to create a grizzly bear calendar that shows what grizzlies do in spring, summer, fall, and winter. For each season, include details about what the grizzlies eat (or don't eat); how they get food; what their appearance is like; and the way they interact with other bears.

Theme 6: Animal Encounters

A Bear Tale

Outline

Write an outline for a fiction story about the life of one particular grizzly bear. Use facts and details from the selection, as well as your own imagination, to help you. Here are some questions you might want to consider as you plan the story.

- male or female?
- its name?
- favorite hibernation spot?
- favorite foods?

- encounters with humans?
- fights for dominance?
- favorite "grizzly games"?

Theme 6: Animal Encounters

Reading Routines

Before You Read . . .

Preview the selection. Read the introduction. Look at the pictures.

As You Read . . .

- **Monitor your comprehension**. Pause periodically to check your understanding of what you have just read.

- **Clarify your understanding**. If you don't understand something, reread, read ahead, or ask questions.

- **Fill in your Topic, Main Idea, and Details Chart**.

- **Think of questions** to discuss with your classmates when you are finished reading.

Theme 6: Animal Encounters

Literature Discussion

Discuss your own questions and the following questions with a group of your classmates:

- Have you ever seen a wild animal in its natural habitat? If so, describe the experience. If not, name an animal you would like to see in the wild, and tell why you want to.

- How do you think the needs of humans for wood, space, and other resources should be balanced with the needs of wild animals?

- Why do you think scientists keep careful records of all tamarins that are reintroduced to the wild?

- Why do you think some people buy wild animals illegally?

Theme 6: Animal Encounters

Exploring the Forest

Sensory Imagery

Sensory images are details an author uses to appeal to a reader's senses. Such imagery helps readers to visualize what they read. On the opening page of this selection, the author uses sensory imagery to give readers a strong impression of what the Brazilian rain forest looks, sounds, and feels like. Identify these details and tell what sense each one appeals to. Use a chart like the one below to record your answers.

Sound	Feeling	Sight

Theme 6: Animal Encounters

Problem and Solution

Create a Chart

Scientists face several problems as they release tamarins into a wooded section of the National Zoo. They must come up with a solution for each one. Reread page 633. Make a chart like the one below, and use it to list each problem the scientists face and the solutions they have devised to overcome each of the problems listed. Compare your chart with those of your classmates when you are finished.

Problem	Solution
protect tamarins from predators	

Theme 6: Animal Encounters

What Happens First?

Summarize Events Graphically

Reread page 638. Pay attention to the steps the observers take to prepare for the release of the tamarins into the wild. Summarize those steps in a flow chart or other graphic organizer that shows the order in which they occurred. Follow these steps:

- Read each paragraph carefully.

- On a piece of paper, jot down each step the observers take.

- Create an organizer, and list the steps in order in your chart.

- When you are finished, share your graphic organizer with your classmates.

Theme 6: Animal Encounters

Reading Routines

Before You Read . . .

Read the title and introduction. Look at the illustrations.

As You Read...

- **Revise your predictions** as you learn more about the characters and events.

- Pause every few pages to **summarize** the story events. Remember to include only the most important details in your summary.

- **Fill in your Conclusions Chart.**

- **Think of questions** to discuss with your classmates when you are finished reading.

Theme 6: Animal Encounters

Literature Discussion

Discuss your own questions and the following questions with a group of your classmates:

- What is your opinion about Sam's decision to stay in the woods during the winter? Explain why you think as you do.

- At the beginning of the story Sam says he feels wonderful. How do you think he feels now? Why?

- Why do you think Sam calls the old wagon axle the "treasure of the treasures"?

- What do you think Sam would have done if Frightful had not returned to him? Why?

Theme 6: Animal Encounters

Will It Work?

Problem Solving

Sam says it takes him three days to figure out how to get his fireplace to work properly. Look back on pages 656 and 657 to identify the problems with the chimney and the solutions Sam uses. Figure out which problem he still must solve. Then work with a partner to make a list of solutions to that problem. Keep your list in mind as you read on to find out what Sam does finally to get the fireplace to work. Compare his solution to the ones you devised.

Theme 6: Animal Encounters

Survival Techniques

Comparing Details

Look back through the story and make a list of all the things the animals do in preparation for the harsh winter months. Then work with a group of your classmates to create another list of ways in which people prepare for winter weather. Think about:

- the way people dress

- the things people do to their cars or other vehicles

- how people prepare their homes

When you have finished, compare animals' preparations with those of humans. How are they alike? How are they different?

Theme 6: Animal Encounters

Observation Checklists

Theme 1

Record observations of student progress
for those areas important to you.

−   = Beginning Understanding
√   = Developing Understanding
√+ = Proficient

Student Names

Earthquake Terror

Comprehension Strategy: Predict/Infer						
Comprehension Skill: Sequence of Events						
Information & Study: Print and Electronic Reference Sources						
Structural Analysis: Base Words						
Phonics: Short Vowels						
Spelling: Short Vowels						
Vocabulary Skill: Thesaurus						
Grammar: Kinds of Sentences; Subjects and Predicates						
Writing Skill: News Article						
Listening/Speaking/Viewing: Panel Discussion						

Reading-Writing Workshop:

Description						

Eye of the Storm: Chasing Storms with Warren Faidley

Comprehension Strategy: Question						
Comprehension Skill: Text Organization						
Information & Study: Library/Print and Electronic Card Catalog						
Structural Analysis: Introduction to Syllabication						
Phonics: /ā/, /ē/, and /ī/						
Spelling: /ā/, /ē/, and /ī/						
Vocabulary Skill: Alphabetical Order/Guide Words						
Grammar: Conjunctions; Compound Sentences						
Writing Skill: Write in Response to a Prompt						
Listening/Speaking/Viewing: Literature Discussion						

Student Names

Record observations of student progress for those areas important to you.

− = Beginning Understanding
√ = Developing Understanding
√+ = Proficient

Volcanoes							
Comprehension Strategy: Monitor/Clarify							
Comprehension Skill: Categorize and Classify							
Information & Study: Graphic Aids: Maps, Globes, Graphs, Tables, Captions, Charts							
Structural Analysis: Roots: -struct and -rupt							
Phonics: Long Vowel Sounds /ō/, /o͞o/, /yo͞o/							
Spelling: Long Vowel Sounds /ō/, /o͞o/, /yo͞o/							
Vocabulary Skill: Definitions							
Grammar: Singular and Plural Nouns; More Plural Nouns							
Writing Skill: Paragraph of Information							
Listening/Speaking/Viewing: Effective Conversations							

General Observation							
Independent Reading							
Independent Writing							
Work Habits							

Theme 2

Observation Checklist

Record observations of student progress for those areas important to you.

- − = Beginning Understanding
- √ = Developing Understanding
- √+ = Proficient

	Student Names					
Michelle Kwan: Heart of a Champion						
Comprehension Strategy: Evaluate						
Comprehension Skill: Fact and Opinion						
Information & Study: Use the Internet/Evaluate Information						
Structural Analysis: Compound Words						
Phonics: Silent Consonants						
Spelling: Compound Words						
Vocabulary Skill: Word Families						
Grammar: Common and Proper Nouns; Singular and Plural Possessive Nouns						
Writing Skill: Write an Announcement						
Listening/Speaking/Viewing: Dramatize a Scene						
Reading-Writing Workshop:						
Personal Essay						
La Bamba						
Comprehension Strategy: Summarize						
Comprehension Skill: Story Structure						
Information & Study: Select the Appropriate Reference Source						
Structural Analysis: Root *spect* and prefix *op-*						
Phonics: The /**ou**/, /**ô**/, and /**oi**/ Sounds						
Spelling: The /**ou**/, /**ô**/, and /**oi**/ Sounds						
Vocabulary Skill: Multiple Meanings						
Grammar: Action Verbs; Direct Objects						
Writing Skill: Write a Summary						
Listening/Speaking/Viewing: Making and Listening to Announcements						

Observation Checklist

Student Names

Record observations of student progress for those areas important to you.

– = Beginning Understanding
√ = Developing Understanding
√+ = Proficient

The Fear Place							
Comprehension Strategy: Predict/Infer							
Comprehension Skill: Predicting Outcomes							
Information & Study: Use Parts of a Book/Index							
Structural Analysis: Suffixes: -ward and -ous							
Phonics: The /ôr/, /âr/, and /är/ Sounds							
Spelling: The /ôr/, /âr/, and /är/ Sounds							
Vocabulary Skill: Homophones							
Grammar: Main Verbs and Helping Verbs; Linking Verbs							
Writing Skill: Clarification Composition							
Listening/Speaking/Viewing: Telling a Story							
Mae Jemison: Space Scientist							
Comprehension Strategy: Monitor/Clarify							
Comprehension Skill: Topic/Main Idea							
Information & Study: Summarize Text Graphically: Venn Diagram, Time Line, Schedule							
Structural Analysis: Suffixes: -ive and -ic							
Phonics: The /ûr/ and /îr/ Sounds							
Spelling: The /ûr/ and /îr/ Sounds							
Vocabulary Skill: Syllables							
Grammar: Verb Tenses (Present, Past, Future); More About Verb Tenses							
Writing Skill: Write a Business Letter							
Listening/Speaking/Viewing: Viewing and Evaluating Media							
General Observation							
Independent Reading							
Independent Writing							
Work Habits							

Theme 3

Student Names

Record observations of student progress for those areas important to you.

– = Beginning Understanding
√ = Developing Understanding
√+ = Proficient

And Then What Happened, Paul Revere?							
Comprehension Strategy: Evaluate							
Comprehension Skill: Author's Viewpoint							
Information & Study: Multiple Sources to Locate Information							
Structural Analysis: Contractions and Possessives							
Phonics: Final /r/							
Spelling: Final /r/							
Vocabulary Skill: Synonyms							
Grammar: Subject-Verb Agreement; Regular and Irregular Verbs							
Writing Skill: Character Sketch							
Listening/Speaking/Viewing: Speak to Persuade							

Reading-Writing Workshop:							
Story							
Katie's Trunk							
Comprehension Strategy: Summarize							
Comprehension Skill: Cause and Effect							
Information & Study: Compare Information in Different Forms							
Structural Analysis: Syllabication: VCCV and VCV patterns							
Phonics: VCCV and VCV patterns							
Spelling: VCCV and VCV patterns							
Vocabulary Skill: Spelling Table/Pronunciation Key							
Grammar: Verb Phrases with have; teach, learn; let, leave; sit, set; can, may							
Writing Skill: Friendly Letter							
Listening/Speaking/Viewing: View and Evaluate Fine Art							

Observation Checklist

Record observations of student progress for those areas important to you.

− = Beginning Understanding
√ = Developing Understanding
√+ = Proficient

Student Names

James Forten						
Comprehension Strategy: Question						
Comprehension Skill: Following Directions						
Information & Study: Adjust Reading Rate/Method of Reading						
Structural Analysis: Prefixes: *sub-* and *sur-*						
Phonics: Final /l/ or /əl/						
Spelling: Final /l/ or /əl/						
Vocabulary Skill: Antonyms						
Grammar: Adjectives; Proper Adjectives						
Writing Skill: Biography						
Listening/Speaking/Viewing: Comparing Information in Various Media						

General Observation						
Independent Reading						
Independent Writing						
Work Habits						

Theme 4

Observation Checklist

Record observations of student progress for those areas important to you.

− = Beginning Understanding
√ = Developing Understanding
√+ = Proficient

Student Names

Mariah Keeps Cool							
Comprehension Strategy: Predict/Infer							
Comprehension Skill: Problem Solving							
Information & Study: Note Taking							
Structural Analysis: Syllabication: VCCCV pattern							
Phonics: VCCCV pattern							
Spelling: VCCCV pattern							
Vocabulary Skill: Base Words and Inflected Forms							
Grammar: Comparing with Adjectives; Comparing with Good and Bad							
Writing Skill: Write a Memo							
Listening/Speaking/Viewing: Giving a Speech							

✏ Reading-Writing Workshop:							
Personal Narrative							

Mom's Best Friend							
Comprehension Strategy: Monitor/Clarify							
Comprehension Skill: Noting Details							
Information & Study: Paraphrasing/Synthesizing							
Structural Analysis: Syllabication: VV pattern							
Phonics: VV pattern							
Spelling: VV pattern							
Vocabulary Skill: Multiple-Meaning Words							
Grammar: Commas in a Series; More Uses for Commas							
Writing Skill: Write Instructions							
Listening/Speaking/Viewing: Explaining a Process							

Observation Checklist

Record observations of student progress for those areas important to you.

- − = Beginning Understanding
- √ = Developing Understanding
- √+ = Proficient

Student Names

Yang the Second and Her Secret Admirers

Comprehension Strategy: Question						
Comprehension Skill: Compare and Contrast						
Information & Study: Evaluate Information for Accuracy and Bias						
Structural Analysis: Inflected Endings: *-ed* and *-ing*						
Phonics: Double Consonants						
Spelling: Inflected Endings: *-ed* and *-ing*						
Vocabulary Skill: Prefixes: *re-, un-, con-/com-, in-/im-*						
Grammar: Interjections; Quotations						
Writing Skill: Write a How-to Paragraph						
Listening/Speaking/Viewing: Speaking on the Telephone						

Dear Mr. Henshaw

Comprehension Strategy: Evaluate						
Comprehension Skill: Making Inferences						
Information & Study: Interview						
Structural Analysis: Words with Suffixes: *-ly, -ness, -ment, -ful, -less*						
Phonics: The /s/ and /z/ Sounds						
Spelling: Words with Suffixes: *-ly, -ness, -ment, -ful, -less*						
Vocabulary Skill: Connotation (Negative or Positive)						
Grammar: Abbreviations; Titles						
Writing Skill: Journal Entry						
Listening/Speaking/Viewing: Making and Listening to Introductions						

General Observation

Independent Reading						
Independent Writing						
Work Habits						

Theme 5

Record observations of student progress for those areas important to you.

− = Beginning Understanding
√ = Developing Understanding
√+ = Proficient

	Student Names						
A Boy Called Slow							
Comprehension Strategy: Predict/Infer							
Comprehension Skill: Drawing Conclusions							
Information & Study: Use a Word Processor to Write a Report							
Structural Analysis: Stressed and Unstressed Syllables							
Phonics: Spelling Unstressed Syllables							
Spelling: Spelling Unstressed Syllables							
Vocabulary Skill: Analogies							
Grammar: Subject and Object Pronouns; Using *I* and *me*							
Writing Skill: Problem-Solution Composition							
Listening/Speaking/Viewing: Listening, Taking Notes and Summarizing							
Reading-Writing Workshop:							
Research Report							
Pioneer Girl							
Comprehension Strategy: Question							
Comprehension Skill: Propaganda							
Information & Study: Compare Information from More Than One Source							
Structural Analysis: Words with a Prefix or a Suffix (*un-, dis-, in-, re-,* and *-ion*)							
Phonics: Word Beginnings: *a-, be-*							
Spelling: Words with a Prefix or a Suffix (*un-, dis-, in-, re-,* and *-ion*)							
Vocabulary Skill: Suffixes							
Grammar: Possessive Pronouns; Contractions with Pronouns							
Writing Skill: Write a Speech							
Listening/Speaking/Viewing: Listening to Resolve Conflicts							

Observation Checklist

Record observations of student progress for those areas important to you.

− = Beginning Understanding
√ = Developing Understanding
√+ = Proficient

	Student Names					
Black Cowboy, Wild Horses						
Comprehension Strategy: Evaluate						
Comprehension Skill: Making Judgments						
Information & Study: Use Multiple Sources of Information to Present Information About a Topic						
Structural Analysis: Review of Syllabication						
Phonics: Final /n/ or /ən/, /chər/, /zhər/						
Spelling: Final /n/ or /ən/, /chər/, /zhər/						
Vocabulary Skill: Parts of Speech						
Grammar: Double Subjects; Using *we* and *us* with Nouns						
Writing Skill: Write an Explanation						
Listening/Speaking/Viewing: Give an Oral Report						
Elena						
Comprehension Strategy: Summarize						
Comprehension Skill: Story Structure						
Information & Study: Create and Organize Disk Files						
Structural Analysis: Words in which final *y* changes to *i*						
Phonics: Words in which final *y* changes to *i*						
Spelling: Words in which final *y* changes to *i*						
Vocabulary Skill: Word Histories						
Grammar: Adverbs; Comparing with Adverbs						
Writing Skill: Write a Compare/Contrast Paragraph						
Listening/Speaking/Viewing: Give a Choral Speaking Presentation						
General Observation						
Independent Reading						
Independent Writing						
Work Habits						

Observation Checklists

Theme 6

Student Names

Record observations of student progress for those areas important to you.

− = Beginning Understanding
√ = Developing Understanding
√+ = Proficient

The Grizzly Bear Family Book						
Comprehension Strategy: Evaluate						
Comprehension Skill: Making Generalizations						
Information & Study: Prepare a Report Using Text, Graphic Aids, and Pictures						
Structural Analysis: More Words with Prefixes (*com-, con-, en-, ex-, pre-, pro-*)						
Phonics: /k/ and /kw/ sounds						
Spelling: More Words with Prefixes (*com-, con-, en-, ex-, pre-, pro-*)						
Vocabulary Skill: Using Context						
Grammar: Contractions with *not*; Negatives						
Writing Skill: Write an Opinion						
Listening/Speaking/Viewing: Multimedia Presentation						

Reading-Writing Workshop:						
Persuasive Essay						

The Golden Lion Tamarin Comes Home						
Comprehension Strategy: Monitor/Clarify						
Comprehension Skill: Topic, Main Idea, Supporting Details						
Information & Study: Evaluate the Effects of Media on Daily Life						
Structural Analysis: Three Syllable Words						
Phonics: Consonant Alternations						
Spelling: Three Syllable Words						
Vocabulary Skill: Variations in Pronunciation						
Grammar: Prepositions; Prepositional Phrases						
Writing Skill: Compare/Contrast Essay						
Listening/Speaking/Viewing: Giving and Listening to Directions						

Record observations of student progress for those areas important to you.

- − = Beginning Understanding
- √ = Developing Understanding
- √+ = Proficient

	Student Names						
My Side of the Mountain							
Comprehension Strategy: Summarize							
Comprehension Skill: Drawing Conclusions							
Information & Study: Complete Applications and Forms							
Structural Analysis: Words with *-ent, -ant, -able, -ible*							
Phonics: Vowel Alternations							
Spelling: Words with *-ent, -ant, -able, -ible*							
Vocabulary Skill: Idioms and Run-on Entries							
Grammar: Object Pronouns in Prepositional Phrases; Object Pronouns (Continued)							
Writing Skill: Answer to an Essay Question							
Listening/Speaking/Viewing: Viewing for Information and Details							
General Observation							
Independent Reading							
Independent Writing							
Work Habits							

Selection Tests and Answer Keys

Earthquake Terror

Write your answers to these questions. Look back at the selection for help.

1. **Strategy Focus: Predict/Infer** Reread the ninth and tenth paragraphs on page 32. ("Jonathan listened . . . ") What clues in the selection helped you predict that Jonathan was hearing the sounds of an earthquake? From these two paragraphs, what can you infer about earthquakes?

   _____

   _____

   _____

2. In the story Jonathan pushes Abby under a fallen tree. List in order three events that happen after this.

   _____

   _____

   _____

Choose the best answer and fill in the circle.

3. Which of the following events happens last in the story?
   - ○ **a.** Jonathan plans what to do when they reach the camper.
   - ○ **b.** Abby notices a cut on her knee.
   - ○ **c.** Jonathan thinks there may be hunters in the woods.
   - ○ **d.** Moose barks and behaves strangely.

4. What is the setting of the story?
   - ○ **a.** the top of a mountain
   - ○ **b.** Jonathan and Abby's yard
   - ○ **c.** an island campground
   - ○ **d.** a bridge across a river

Test Continues ➡

Earthquake Terror (continued)

5. What causes Moose to bark at Jonathan when they begin to walk to the camper?

   ○ **a.** Moose senses the changes in the earth.

   ○ **b.** Moose does not like to wear the leash.

   ○ **c.** Moose feels that Jonathan is walking too fast.

   ○ **d.** Moose is afraid that Jonathan is lost.

Read the sentence and choose the best answer.

6. During the earthquake, Jonathan feels as if the earth is <u>moving in waves</u>. In this sentence, what does the earth seem to be doing?

   ○ **a.** swaying

   ○ **b.** undulating

   ○ **c.** transforming

   ○ **d.** billowing

7. *As Jonathan scrambled across the unsteady ground, he clenched his teeth, bracing himself for the <u>impact</u>.*

   What does the word *impact* mean in this sentence?

   ○ **a.** the striking of one object against another

   ○ **b.** a long and difficult climb

   ○ **c.** a long wait for something unpleasant

   ○ **d.** the sudden movement of the ground

Eye of the Storm: Chasing Storms with Warren Faidley

Write your answers to these questions. Look back at the selection for help.

1. **Strategy Focus: Question** Reread the sixth paragraph on page 59. ("For twenty minutes . . .") What question could you ask about this passage? Write one question and its answer.

   _____

   _____

   _____

2. What do you expect after reading the heading "What Happens to Warren's Photos After He Takes Them?" How would you answer the question it asks?

   _____

   _____

   _____

Choose the best answer and fill in the circle.

3. What do the headings in Warren's diary tell you?
   - ○ **a.** The headings tell what the tornado will do next.
   - ○ **b.** The headings tell the time and place of each entry.
   - ○ **c.** The headings tell about the photographs Warren will take.
   - ○ **d.** The headings tell how Warren feels as he watches the tornado.

Test Continues ➡

Eye of the Storm: Chasing Storms with Warren Faidley (continued)

4. Which of these sentences from the story states an opinion?

  ○ **a.** *It sounded as if the sky were being torn apart.*

  ○ **b.** *As these mini-tornadoes spin, they kick up dust of their own.*

  ○ **c.** *Storms are caused by certain kinds of weather patterns.*

  ○ **d.** *Warren's business is called a stock photo agency.*

5. Which of these events happens first?

  ○ **a.** Warren rides a bicycle into a dust whirlwind.

  ○ **b.** Warren takes a photograph of a spectacular lightning bolt.

  ○ **c.** *Life* magazine publishes one of Warren's photos.

  ○ **d.** Warren becomes interested in taking pictures of hurricanes.

Read the sentence and choose the best answer.

6. Tornadoes can form when masses of warm air and cool air <u>bump into each other.</u>

  Tornadoes can form when the air masses _____.

  ○ **a.** separate

  ○ **b.** collide

  ○ **c.** circulate

  ○ **d.** assemble

7. The winds in a tornado <u>rotate</u> at great speeds.

  What does the word *rotate* mean?

  ○ **a.** spin

  ○ **b.** jump

  ○ **c.** blow

  ○ **d.** start

Volcanoes

Write your answers to these questions. Look back at the selection for help.

1. **Strategy Focus: Monitor/Clarify** How did you use the photos and maps in the selection to clarify what you read? Give at least one example.

   _____

   _____

   _____

2. Describe the four groups of volcanoes.

   _____

   _____

   _____

   _____

Choose the best answer and fill in the circle.

3. Which of these is <u>not</u> on the North American plate?

   ○ **a.** Canada

   ○ **b.** the Pacific Ocean

   ○ **c.** the United States

   ○ **d.** Mexico

4. Most of the volcanoes in the world are _____.

   ○ **a.** cinder cone volcanoes

   ○ **b.** strato-volcanoes

   ○ **c.** shield volcanoes

   ○ **d.** dome volcanoes

Test Continues ➡

Volcanoes (continued)

5. Which sentence states the main idea of the first paragraph on page 88?

   ○ **a.** *Hundreds of houses and cabins were destroyed, leaving many people homeless.*

   ○ **b.** *Miles of highways, roads, and railways were badly damaged.*

   ○ **c.** *The eruption of Mount St. Helens was the most destructive in the history of the United States.*

   ○ **d.** *Sixty people lost their lives as hot gases, rocks, and ashes covered an area of two hundred thirty square miles.*

Read the sentence and choose the best answer.

6. *Further eruptions add more layers of ashes and* <u>cinders</u>*, followed by more layers of lava.*

   What does the word *cinders* mean in this sentence?

   ○ **a.** fiery explosions

   ○ **b.** parts of a mountain

   ○ **c.** charred bits of rock

   ○ **d.** gases from the earth

7. Hot <u>magma</u> pushes up between the plates.
   What is *magma*?

   ○ **a.** tar and ash

   ○ **b.** a type of gas

   ○ **c.** streams of water

   ○ **d.** melted rock

Michelle Kwan: Heart of a Champion

Write your answers to these questions. Look back at the selection for help.

1. **Strategy Focus: Evaluate** Reread the second paragraph on page 147. Do you like the way the author speaks to the reader? Explain.

   _____

   _____

   _____

2. Write one fact that you learned from the selection.

   _____

   _____

   _____

Choose the best answer and fill in the circle.

3. Which of these sentences from the selection states an opinion?

   ○ **a.** *Frank went off to a coaches' conference in Canada for a week.*

   ○ **b.** *Every month there's at least one major competition, plus exhibitions.*

   ○ **c.** *Most skaters have really ugly feet.*

   ○ **d.** *The USFSA gave us some support, too.*

4. Which of these sentences is a fact that could be proved?

   ○ **a.** *Every skater has qualities that make him or her special.*

   ○ **b.** *The life of a top-level skater is intense.*

   ○ **c.** *I was young and I looked it.*

   ○ **d.** *Each skater has two programs for competitions.*

Test Continues ➡

Michelle Kwan: Heart of a Champion (continued)

5. Which of these methods does Michelle use to help readers understand the story?

   ○ **a.** She tells the events in order.

   ○ **b.** She tells her story from another person's point of view.

   ○ **c.** She includes questions and answers.

   ○ **d.** She includes diagrams that show the reader how to skate.

Read the sentence and choose the best answer.

6. Michelle was able to <u>compete</u> with older skaters.
   What does *compete* mean in this sentence?

   ○ **a.** take part in a contest

   ○ **b.** skate in a group

   ○ **c.** train for longer periods of time

   ○ **d.** travel with her team

7. The rules state that a long program and a short program are <u>required</u>.
   What does this tell us about the long and short programs?

   ○ **a.** They are simple.

   ○ **b.** They are complex.

   ○ **c.** They are important.

   ○ **d.** They are necessary.

La Bamba

Write your answers to these questions. Look back at the selection for help.

1. **Strategy Focus: Summarize** Describe Manuel's performance in the talent show.

   _____

   _____

   _____

2. What important role does Benny play in the story?

   _____

   _____

   _____

Choose the best answer and fill in the circle.

3. Which of the following is the most important moment in the story?
   - ○ **a.** Manuel forgets his math workbook.
   - ○ **b.** Manuel tries a few dance steps on stage.
   - ○ **c.** Manuel's "La Bamba" record gets stuck.
   - ○ **d.** Manuel remembers when his flashlight didn't work.

4. What causes Manuel to enter the talent show?
   - ○ **a.** He wants to learn a new skill.
   - ○ **b.** Mr. Roybal asks him to help out.
   - ○ **c.** He wants to spend time with Benny.
   - ○ **d.** He yearns for the limelight.

Test Continues ➡

La Bamba (continued)

5. What most surprises Manuel after the talent show?

○ **a.** He sees his brother Mario wearing his shirt.

○ **b.** People tell him that they liked his act.

○ **c.** A teacher brings cookies and punch.

○ **d.** Mr. Roybal rips the needle across the record.

Read the sentence and choose the best answer.

6. From the stage Manuel hears the applause.
   What does this mean people are doing?

○ **a.** talking

○ **b.** singing

○ **c.** clapping

○ **d.** screaming

7. Benny has musical talent.
   What does this mean that Benny has?

○ **a.** a musical instrument

○ **b.** difficulty with music

○ **c.** skills that need practice

○ **d.** a natural ability

The Fear Place

Write your answers to these questions. Look back at the selection for help.

1. **Strategy Focus: Predict/Infer** Reread the third paragraph on page 197. What clues in this paragraph suggest that Doug will successfully walk around the ledge? Explain.

   _____

   _____

   _____

2. Do you think Doug would have made it around the ledge if Charlie hadn't been there to show him how? Why or why not?

   _____

   _____

   _____

Choose the best answer and fill in the circle.

3. What do you think is most likely to happen now that Doug has successfully made it past the ledge?

   ○ **a.** Doug won't be able to get around the ledge on the way back.

   ○ **b.** Doug will feel much more sure of himself on the way back.

   ○ **c.** Doug will feel scared of Charlie.

   ○ **d.** Doug will feel too weak to help Gordie.

4. Why does Doug concentrate on rocks as he climbs?

   ○ **a.** He is interested in geology.

   ○ **b.** He is trying to remember the right names.

   ○ **c.** He is trying to keep his mind from worrying.

   ○ **d.** He is trying to find the right path.

Test Continues ➡

The Fear Place (continued)

5. Doug thinks of the narrow ledge as a _____.

   ○ **a.** ribbon made of stone

   ○ **b.** chalk line on the sidewalk

   ○ **c.** thin wire high in the air

   ○ **d.** stripe in the middle of a road

Read the sentence and choose the best answer.

6. *He was dismayed that he was thirsty again.*
   What does the word *dismayed* mean in this sentence?

   ○ **a.** troubled

   ○ **b.** shocked

   ○ **c.** excited

   ○ **d.** happy

7. Doug was <u>cautious</u> as he climbed higher and higher.
   How was Doug feeling?

   ○ **a.** frantic

   ○ **b.** reckless

   ○ **c.** confident

   ○ **d.** careful

Mae Jemison: Space Scientist

Write your answers to these questions. Look back at the selection for help.

1. **Strategy Focus: Monitor/Clarify** What did you do when you read something in the selection that you did not understand right away? Give at least one example.

   _____

   _____

   _____

2. How would you describe the topic of this selection to a friend?

   _____

   _____

   _____

Choose the best answer and fill in the circle.

3. Which detail best supports the main idea that Jemison likes challenges?

   ○ **a.** Jemison was curious about the effects of weightlessness on bone cells.

   ○ **b.** Jemison learned a lot from her experiences in the Peace Corps.

   ○ **c.** Jemison flew in a special training jet that simulates zero gravity.

   ○ **d.** Jemison moved to Houston, Texas, to begin her training.

4. Which of these events happened first?

   ○ **a.** Mae Jemison graduated from Stanford University.

   ○ **b.** Mae Jemison started a business called The Jemison Group.

   ○ **c.** Mae Jemison flew on the *Endeavour*.

   ○ **d.** Mae Jemison became a doctor.

Test Continues ➡

Mae Jemison: Space Scientist (continued)

5. Which of these does <u>not</u> describe Mae Jemison?

    ○ **a.** scientist

    ○ **b.** lawyer

    ○ **c.** astronaut

    ○ **d.** doctor

Read the sentence and choose the best answer.

6. *In the 1970s, NASA designed the space shuttle as the first <u>reusable</u> spacecraft.*

    What does the word *reusable* mean in this sentence?

    ○ **a.** able to carry people

    ○ **b.** having wings

    ○ **c.** able to be used again

    ○ **d.** having controls

7. The space shuttle *Endeavour* made 127 <u>orbits</u> of Earth.

    What does this mean the *Endeavour* did?

    ○ **a.** left Earth 127 times

    ○ **b.** took 127 pictures of Earth

    ○ **c.** conducted 127 experiments for scientists on Earth

    ○ **d.** made 127 trips around Earth

And Then What Happened, Paul Revere?

Write your answers to these questions. Look back at the selection for help.

1. **Strategy Focus: Evaluate** What do you like best about the way the author describes Paul Revere?

_____

_____

_____

2. Why do you think the author wrote this story about Paul Revere?

_____

_____

_____

Choose the best answer and fill in the circle.

3. Which of these states an opinion the author probably holds?

   ○ **a.** Boston was a busy city during the time that Paul Revere lived.

   ○ **b.** Paul Revere played an important role in the American Revolution.

   ○ **c.** Paul Revere rang the bell in the North Church on many occasions.

   ○ **d.** Paul Revere was once held prisoner by English soldiers.

4. More often than not, Paul Revere liked to find _____.

   ○ **a.** silence

   ○ **b.** calm

   ○ **c.** excitement

   ○ **d.** movement

Test Continues ➡

And Then What Happened, Paul Revere? (continued)

Read the sentence and choose the best answer.

5. Paul Revere was an <u>express</u> rider who spread the news of Patriot activities.

What does this mean about his rides?

○ **a.** They went from town to town.

○ **b.** They were rapid and made few or no stops.

○ **c.** They covered great distances.

○ **d.** They were not necessary.

6. The colonists <u>opposed</u> the tax on tea.

How did they feel about this tax?

○ **a.** They were against it.

○ **b.** They supported it.

○ **c.** They enjoyed it.

○ **d.** They wanted to keep it.

7. The British ship carried its <u>cargo</u> into the Boston harbor.

What does the word *cargo* mean in this sentence?

○ **a.** a crew

○ **b.** tea

○ **c.** freight

○ **d.** money

Katie's Trunk

Write your answers to these questions. Look back at the selection for help.

1. **Strategy Focus: Summarize** What happens after Katie leaves her family in the woods?

   _____

   _____

   _____

2. What causes Katie to run back into the house?

   _____

   _____

   _____

Choose the best answer and fill in the circle.

3. Why does Katie hide in her mother's trunk?

   ○ **a.** She wants to protect her family.

   ○ **b.** She hears rebels coming in the door.

   ○ **c.** The front door is locked.

   ○ **d.** She does not want to hide in the woods.

4. Why does John Warren leave the trunk open when he leaves the house?

   ○ **a.** He forgets to close it.

   ○ **b.** He wants Katie to be able to breathe.

   ○ **c.** He is in a big rush.

   ○ **d.** He does not want to put everything away.

Test Continues ➡

Name: _____

Katie's Trunk (continued)

5. What problem does Katie's family face because they are Tories?

   ○ **a.** They cannot hold office in the community.

   ○ **b.** They must pay higher taxes than their neighbors.

   ○ **c.** They must march and drill each day in the meadow.

   ○ **d.** Many neighbors and former friends won't speak to them.

Read the sentence and choose the best answer.

6. Katie heard gunfire during the short fight between the Tories and the rebels.

   Which word below has the same meaning as *short fight*?

   ○ **a.** skirmish

   ○ **b.** conversation

   ○ **c.** vehicle

   ○ **d.** orchestra

7. Papa peered out the window.

   What does the word *peered* mean in this sentence?

   ○ **a.** fell

   ○ **b.** looked

   ○ **c.** leaned

   ○ **d.** called

Name: _____

James Forten

Write your answers to these questions. Look back at the selection for help.

1. **Strategy Focus: Question** Reread the third through sixth paragraphs of the selection on pages 318 through 320. What question could you ask after reading these paragraphs? Write one question and its answer.

   _____

   _____

   _____

2. What steps did the men on the Royal Louis follow in preparing the cannons?

   _____

   _____

   _____

Choose the best answer and fill in the circle.

3. What is the main topic of this selection?

   ○ **a.** ships at sea

   ○ **b.** a man who helped fight for America

   ○ **c.** the career of a sailmaker's father

   ○ **d.** Quaker schools

4. Which of these statements shows the author's viewpoint?

   ○ **a.** The people who fought in the American Revolution weren't very brave.

   ○ **b.** James Forten was not a hero, but he fought well for his country.

   ○ **c.** The Royal Louis was captured because its captain was not careful.

   ○ **d.** James Forten was too young to be allowed to go to sea at age fourteen.

Test Continues ➡

James Forten (continued)

5. Which detail below explains why Forten became interested in going to sea?

   ○ **a.** *Sometimes he heard talk about naval battles, and he tried to imagine what they must have been like.*

   ○ **b.** *The colonies had few ships of their own to fight against the powerful British navy . . .*

   ○ **c.** *After what must have seemed forever with the two ships tacking about each other like angry cats, the Active lowered its flag.*

   ○ **d.** *The crew carried more ammunition aboard, more powder, and fresh provisions.*

Read the sentence and choose the best answer.

6. Bridges <u>encouraged</u> James Forten throughout his life.

   What does this mean that Bridges did for Forten?

   ○ **a.** ignored him

   ○ **b.** ordered him around

   ○ **c.** supported his plans

   ○ **d.** paid him

7. Beasley's son played a game with the <u>captives</u> on the ship.

   What does the word *captives* mean in this sentence?

   ○ **a.** young men

   ○ **b.** sailors who work below deck

   ○ **c.** crew

   ○ **d.** prisoners

Mariah Keeps Cool

Write your answers to these questions. Look back at the selection for help.

1. **Strategy Focus: Predict/Infer** What clues help you predict that Lynn will get out of bed on her birthday?

   _____

   _____

   _____

2. What do Mariah and Brandon do to solve the problems caused by Lynn showing up at Brandon's house?

   _____

   _____

   _____

Choose the best answer and fill in the circle.

3. How does Mariah get Lynn out of the house so that Denise can join the girls at Brandon's?

   ○ **a.** She arranges for the homeless shelter to call Lynn.

   ○ **b.** She asks her mother to send Lynn on an errand.

   ○ **c.** She takes Lynn to the bookstore.

   ○ **d.** She takes Lynn out for lunch.

4. Why does Denise hide when Lynn comes to Brandon's house?

   ○ **a.** She knows that Lynn is angry with her.

   ○ **b.** She knows that Lynn will wonder why she is there.

   ○ **c.** She doesn't want to swim in Brandon's pool.

   ○ **d.** She wants Brandon's mother to try to find her.

Test Continues ➡

Name: _____

Mariah Keeps Cool (continued)

5. Where does the party take place?

   ○ **a.** at the town pool

   ○ **b.** at the rec center

   ○ **c.** at Brandon's house

   ○ **d.** in Mariah's yard

Read the sentence and choose the best answer.

6. *Today she was going to show the Friendly Five how to make paper flowers to* <u>*decorate*</u> *their yard for the party.*

   What does the word *decorate* mean in this sentence?

   ○ **a.** to make something from paper

   ○ **b.** to plant seeds

   ○ **c.** to make something look pretty

   ○ **d.** to give water to plants

7. Mariah wants to have a <u>celebration</u> for Lynn's birthday.

   What does Mariah want to have?

   ○ **a.** a cake

   ○ **b.** an invitation

   ○ **c.** a gift

   ○ **d.** a party

Selection Tests

Mom's Best Friend

Write your answers to these questions. Look back at the selection for help.

1. **Strategy Focus: Monitor/Clarify** What did you do to help clarify parts of the selection that you did not understand? Give at least one example.

   _____

   _____

   _____

2. Describe Ursula, using what you learned from the pictures and the text.

   _____

   _____

   _____

Choose the best answer and fill in the circle.

3. What does Ursula do when she first meets Sally and Joel?
   - ○ **a.** She runs and hides under Sally's bed.
   - ○ **b.** She jumps up on them and nearly knocks them over.
   - ○ **c.** She sits down, becomes very still, and stares at them.
   - ○ **d.** She flops down on the floor and begins to roll around.

4. What is the first step of "loneliness training"?
   - ○ **a.** Mom lets Sally introduce one friend to Ursula.
   - ○ **b.** Mom leaves Ursula at guide school for two weeks.
   - ○ **c.** Mom leaves Ursula home alone and goes jogging with Dad.
   - ○ **d.** Mom does not let Ursula go outside for two weeks.

Test Continues ➡

Mom's Best Friend (continued)

5. What does Mom do if Ursula acts cute and causes a stranger to pet her?

   ○ **a.** Mom scolds Ursula and asks the stranger not to pet her.

   ○ **b.** Mom praises Ursula and lets the stranger pet her.

   ○ **c.** Mom takes Ursula home.

   ○ **d.** Mom tells the stranger to go away.

Read the sentence and choose the best answer.

6. It is Ursula's <u>instinct</u> to protect Mom from danger.
   This means that protecting Mom _____.

   ○ **a.** comes naturally

   ○ **b.** must be learned

   ○ **c.** is hard work

   ○ **d.** is Ursula's job to do alone

7. *Every day Mom and Ursula made two trips. Every week they* <u>*mastered*</u> *new routes.*
   Which of the following is another word for *mastered*?

   ○ **a.** followed

   ○ **b.** found

   ○ **c.** learned

   ○ **d.** walked

Yang the Second and Her Secret Admirers

Write your answers to these questions. Look back at the selection for help.

1. **Strategy Focus: Question** Reread the sixth paragraph on page 400. ("Arranging for Paul…") What question could you ask a classmate after reading this paragraph? Write one question and its answer.

    _____

    _____

    _____

2. How are Yingtao and Paul alike? How are they different?

    _____

    _____

    _____

Choose the best answer and fill in the circle.

3. How has Second Sister changed since moving to the United States?
    - ○ **a.** She used to have lots of friends. Now she has very few friends.
    - ○ **b.** She used to love playing the *erhu*. Now she refuses to play music.
    - ○ **c.** She used to dislike math. Now she loves math.
    - ○ **d.** She used to help with the chores. Now she stays in her room and mopes.

4. Why didn't Kim and Third Sister talk when they were near the tyrannosaurus?
    - ○ **a.** Paul was standing too close to them.
    - ○ **b.** They could not see each other.
    - ○ **c.** The dinosaur was roaring too loudly.
    - ○ **d.** They wanted to see where Paul went next.

Test Continues ➡

Name: _____

Yang the Second and Her Secret Admirers (continued)

5. The instrument that Yinglan played at school is most like which instrument?

   ○ **a.** a drum

   ○ **b.** a violin

   ○ **c.** a flute

   ○ **d.** a guitar

Read the sentence and choose the best answer.

6. Second Sister is very proud of her Chinese <u>heritage</u>.

   What is Second Sister proud of?

   ○ **a.** her Chinese teacher

   ○ **b.** her family

   ○ **c.** her Chinese traditions

   ○ **d.** her musical ability

7. *Second Sister likes the costumes and music when she goes to a Chinese <u>opera</u>.*

   What does the word *opera* mean in this sentence?

   ○ **a.** a clever song

   ○ **b.** a dress shop

   ○ **c.** a play with singing

   ○ **d.** a movie with poetry

Dear Mr. Henshaw

Write your answers to these questions. Look back at the selection for help.

1. **Strategy Focus: Evaluate** If you were going to reread a part of this selection just for fun, which part would it be? Explain.

_____

_____

_____

2. How does Leigh feel after having lunch with Angela Badger? Explain how you know.

_____

_____

_____

Choose the best answer and fill in the circle.

3. What is the most likely reason that Leigh keeps a diary?
   - ○ **a.** He has trouble remembering the things that happen.
   - ○ **b.** Writing helps him sort through his feelings about things.
   - ○ **c.** His teacher gave his class an assignment to write in a diary.
   - ○ **d.** His father suggested that Leigh write in his diary.

4. Which sentence best describes Angela Badger?
   - ○ **a.** She is an honest woman.
   - ○ **b.** She is a boring writer.
   - ○ **c.** She likes to talk about herself.
   - ○ **d.** She is a shy woman.

Test Continues ➡

Dear Mr. Henshaw (continued)

5. With which of these statements would Angela Badger probably agree?

   ○ **a.** Writers should write only imaginary stories.

   ○ **b.** Writers should write about things they feel strongly about.

   ○ **c.** It is not a good idea to include many details in a story.

   ○ **d.** Children's stories are not as interesting as stories written by adults.

Read the sentence and choose the best answer.

6. Leigh likes to write about <u>things that happen to him</u>.
   What does he like to write about?

   ○ **a.** his experiences

   ○ **b.** his relatives

   ○ **c.** his mistakes

   ○ **d.** his stories

7. Leigh writes <u>details that tell about</u> the time he rode in his father's truck.
   Which of the following is another word for *details that tell about*?

   ○ **a.** an inspection

   ○ **b.** a description

   ○ **c.** a combination

   ○ **d.** an equation

Name: _____

A Boy Called Slow

Write your answers to these questions. Look back at the selection for help.

1. **Strategy Focus: Predict/Infer** What clues from the story helped you predict that Slow would play an important role in the battle with the Crow?

    _____

    _____

    _____

2. How is Slow like his father?

    _____

    _____

    _____

Choose the best answer and fill in the circle.

3. What might you guess about Returns Again?

    ○ **a.** He unfairly favors his own son at times.

    ○ **b.** He is a leader of his people.

    ○ **c.** He cannot hunt as skillfully as others.

    ○ **d.** He loves his sons more than his daughters.

4. How is Slow different from other boys his age?

    ○ **a.** He is stronger.

    ○ **b.** He is taller.

    ○ **c.** He shares more food.

    ○ **d.** He has more names.

Test Continues ➡

A Boy Called Slow (continued)

5. What is Slow's name when he grows up?

   ○ **a.** Sitting Bull

   ○ **b.** Gray Pony

   ○ **c.** Swift Crow

   ○ **d.** Strike the Enemy

Read the sentence and choose the best answer.

6. *It was the* <u>*custom*</u> *in those days to give a childhood name.*

   What does the word *custom* mean in this sentence?

   ○ **a.** a price or fee

   ○ **b.** a story or tale

   ○ **c.** a tradition or way

   ○ **d.** a challenge or test

7. Slow wanted to join the men in an <u>attack in which they would take property.</u>

   Which of the following is another word for this kind of attack?

   ○ **a.** treaty

   ○ **b.** realm

   ○ **c.** raid

   ○ **d.** gathering

Name: _____

Pioneer Girl

Write your answers to these questions. Look back at the selection for help.

1. **Strategy Focus: Question** Reread the second paragraph on page 505. What question could you ask a classmate after reading this paragraph? Write one question and its answer.

   _____

   _____

   _____

2. How does the poster on page 500 convince people to buy land in Nebraska?

   _____

   _____

   _____

Choose the best answer and fill in the circle.

3. Which of the following could you say about Poppie?
   - ○ **a.** He always looks at the bright side of things.
   - ○ **b.** He is often very impatient.
   - ○ **c.** He would rather live in the East than in Nebraska.
   - ○ **d.** He feels that he should be able to run the farm by himself.

4. You might predict that over the years the McCance family _____.
   - ○ **a.** keeps to themselves more and more
   - ○ **b.** loses their farm to the Yoders
   - ○ **c.** has to work harder and harder to make ends meet
   - ○ **d.** makes new friends as more people settle nearby

Test Continues ➡

Name: _____

Pioneer Girl (continued)

5. Why did the writers of the poster on page 500 most likely include the phrase *commerce and wealth*?

   ○ **a.** to make readers feel that they could become rich

   ○ **b.** to give readers information about the land

   ○ **c.** to describe the land for people who hadn't seen it

   ○ **d.** to make readers feel important

Read the sentence and choose the best answer.

6. The McCance <u>homestead</u> was located in Nebraska.
   What does the word *homestead* mean in this sentence?

   ○ **a.** a pioneer family's farmhouse, buildings, and land

   ○ **b.** the place from which a pioneer family had come

   ○ **c.** the town in which a pioneer family settled

   ○ **d.** a pioneer family's cattle, chickens, and other livestock

7. Some of the houses were made of <u>sod</u>.
   In this sentence, the word *sod* means _____.

   ○ **a.** bricks made of sand

   ○ **b.** pieces of wood

   ○ **c.** leaves and sticks

   ○ **d.** grassy soil

Black Cowboy, Wild Horses

Write your answers to these questions. Look back at the selection for help.

1. **Strategy Focus: Evaluate** Reread the third paragraph on page 535. Do you think the author does a good job of writing about this dangerous situation? Explain your answer.

   _____

   _____

   _____

2. What do you admire most about Bob? Why?

   _____

   _____

   _____

Choose the best answer and fill in the circle.

3. Why does Bob spend several days following the herd?

   ○ **a.** He has trouble following the horses' tracks.

   ○ **b.** He is waiting for the horses to move closer to the ranch.

   ○ **c.** He wants the horses to get used to him being around.

   ○ **d.** The horses run a great distance away when they see a snake.

4. Based on the details in the story, which judgment about Bob is most accurate?

   ○ **a.** He is brave.

   ○ **b.** He is generous.

   ○ **c.** He is honest.

   ○ **d.** He is unhappy.

Test Continues ➡

Name: _____

Black Cowboy, Wild Horses (continued)

5. With which of these statements would the author most likely agree?

○ **a.** Bob was sometimes impatient with the horses.

○ **b.** Bob should have taken more men with him.

○ **c.** Wild mustangs are easy to round up.

○ **d.** It takes special skills to track wild mustangs.

Read the sentence and choose the best answer.

6. The horses <u>milled</u> about as they sensed danger.
What did the horses do?

○ **a.** They nudged one another.

○ **b.** They pawed at the ground.

○ **c.** They trotted away.

○ **d.** They moved nervously.

7. Bob rode Warrior up the <u>high bank</u> and looked at the ranch below.
Which of the following is another word for *high bank*?

○ **a.** peak

○ **b.** valley

○ **c.** river's edge

○ **d.** bluff

Name: _____

Elena

Write your answers to these questions. Look back at the selection for help.

1. **Strategy Focus: Summarize** What happens when the soldiers come to the house and Elena opens the door?

   _____

   _____

   _____

2. Summarize two events in the story. Tell what the events show about Elena.

   _____

   _____

   _____

Choose the best answer and fill in the circle.

3. Which sentence summarizes the first important event in the story?

   ○ **a.** Pablo mounts his horse.

   ○ **b.** Pablo's horse falls down a ravine.

   ○ **c.** Pablo dies in his bed.

   ○ **d.** Elena goes crazy with grief.

4. What does the family do when they run out of money?

   ○ **a.** Esteban joins the army and Elena runs a boardinghouse.

   ○ **b.** Esteban picks fruit and Elena runs a boardinghouse.

   ○ **c.** Esteban picks fruit and Elena goes back to Mexico.

   ○ **d.** Esteban makes sombreros and Elena picks fruit.

Test Continues ➡

Name: _____

Elena (continued)

5. What happens to the town where the family had lived in Mexico?

   ○ **a.** It is completely destroyed.

   ○ **b.** It becomes a bustling city.

   ○ **c.** It stays just the same as it always was.

   ○ **d.** It becomes the home of Pancho Villa.

Read the sentence and choose the best answer.

6. Pancho Villa expressed his sympathy for Elena's loss.
   What did Pancho Villa express?

   ○ **a.** his annoyance

   ○ **b.** his condolences

   ○ **c.** his discomfort

   ○ **d.** his anxiety

7. After Pablo's death, Elena's appearance completely changed.
   What happened to her appearance?

   ○ **a.** It was destroyed.

   ○ **b.** It was transformed.

   ○ **c.** It was injured.

   ○ **d.** It was unsettled.

The Grizzly Bear Family Book

Write your answers to these questions. Look back at the selection for help.

1. **Strategy Focus: Evaluate** The author uses the first-person point of view to write about his own experiences. What do you like or dislike about this method?

   _____

   _____

   _____

2. What generalization can you make about the way mother bears treat their cubs?

   _____

   _____

   _____

Choose the best answer and fill in the circle.

3. Which of these sentences is a generalization about people's feelings toward bears?

   ○ **a.** *People have such fearful images of bears.*

   ○ **b.** *I was startled, but the bear must have been even more surprised.*

   ○ **c.** *Imagine meeting a grizzly bear in the wild.*

   ○ **d.** *"Don't bump heads with a bear when you go blueberry picking!"*

4. With which generalization would the author most likely agree?

   ○ **a.** Bears will always attack humans.

   ○ **b.** Most states have set aside enough natural areas for wildlife.

   ○ **c.** Winter in Alaska is the most beautiful season of all.

   ○ **d.** Alaskan animals are interesting to photograph.

Test Continues ➡

The Grizzly Bear Family Book (continued)

5. Which of the following statements is a fact?

   ○ **a.** *An 850-pound bear chasing a 2-pound squirrel is a truly comical sight.*

   ○ **b.** *Bears seem to like soapberries best of all.*

   ○ **c.** *One bear may consume 200,000 berries in a single day!*

   ○ **d.** *In early spring, grizzly bears also enjoy life to its fullest.*

Read the sentence and choose the best answer.

6. Animals that live in the Alaskan <u>wilderness</u> can adapt to cold weather.

   What kind of region does the word *wilderness* describe?

   ○ **a.** a region that has many animals

   ○ **b.** a region that is close to a city

   ○ **c.** a region that is in its natural state

   ○ **d.** a region that has few plants

7. Bears and other animals in the wild view humans with <u>caution</u>.

   How do they view humans?

   ○ **a.** with confidence

   ○ **b.** with alarm

   ○ **c.** with surprise

   ○ **d.** with wariness

Name: _____

The Golden Lion Tamarin Comes Home

Write your answers to these questions. Look back at the selection for help.

1. **Strategy Focus: Monitor/Clarify** Reread page 634. Why are the team's notes sent to the zoo? What could you do if you did not know the answer?

   _____

   _____

   _____

2. What does the title of this selection mean?

   _____

   _____

   _____

Choose the best answer and fill in the circle.

3. Reread the first paragraph on page 632. What is the main idea of the paragraph?

   ○ **a.** *These animals do not have the skills to survive in the wild on their own.*

   ○ **b.** *It has never leaped from a vine to a delicate tree branch that sways under its weight.*

   ○ **c.** *It hasn't experienced weather changes — cold, rain, thunder, and lightning.*

   ○ **d.** *It doesn't know how to forage for its food.*

4. Reread page 641. Choose the sentence that supports this main idea: Only about 30 percent of all reintroduced tamarins survive more than two years.

   ○ **a.** *They are more acrobatic and confident as they leap from limb to limb.*

   ○ **b.** *Bit by bit, the family becomes familiar with the rain forest, the younger ones adapting faster than the parents.*

   ○ **c.** *Some die by eating poisonous fruits or snakes.*

   ○ **d.** *When the tamarins become independent, all feeding is stopped.*

   Test Continues ➡

Name: _____

The Golden Lion Tamarin Comes Home (continued)

5. Choose the sentence that supports the following generalization: The observers are prepared for emergencies.

   ○ **a.** *In order not to give the tamarins human characteristics, the observers do not give them names.*

   ○ **b.** *The observation team is split into two groups.*

   ○ **c.** *Each carries a canteen and a machete on a belt, as well as a backpack with food, rain gear, a snakebite kit, and mosquito repellent.*

   ○ **d.** *Below, Andreia glances at her watch and writes in her notebook.*

Read the sentence and choose the best answer.

6. Some tamarins <u>live in zoos</u>.

   What can you call these tamarins?

   ○ **a.** captive tamarins

   ○ **b.** threatening tamarins

   ○ **c.** attractive tamarins

   ○ **d.** extraordinary tamarins

7. The scientists face a <u>problem without an easy answer</u>.

   What is another word for this kind of problem?

   ○ **a.** plight

   ○ **b.** situation

   ○ **c.** caution

   ○ **d.** dilemma

Name: _____

My Side of the Mountain

Write your answers to these questions. Look back at the selection for help.

1. **Strategy Focus: Summarize** What happens after Sam is awakened by a screaming noise and discovers animals in his tree?

   _____

   _____

   _____

2. After Sam drags the clay back to the tree, he spends three days building the fireplace and fixing it so that it doesn't smoke. What does this tell you about Sam?

   _____

   _____

   _____

Choose the best answer and fill in the circle.

3. Which conclusion about Sam is best supported by details in the story?
   - ○ **a.** He prefers to be alone.
   - ○ **b.** He respects wild animals.
   - ○ **c.** He is funny and selfish.
   - ○ **d.** He is lazy and angry.

4. When Sam says the "mountaintop was full of songs and twittering and flashing wings," you might conclude that he _____.
   - ○ **a.** does not like birds
   - ○ **b.** likes birds
   - ○ **c.** likes to sing songs
   - ○ **d.** thinks that some birds are leaving the mountaintop

Test Continues ➡

My Side of the Mountain (continued)

5. What is the last step in Sam's fireplace-making process?
   - ○ **a.** holding up the chimney funnel with a flat stone
   - ○ **b.** hauling the clay up the mountain in a pair of pants
   - ○ **c.** adding grasses into the clay to help it hold its own weight
   - ○ **d.** cutting out more knotholes in the tree

Read the sentence and choose the best answer.

6. Sam <u>fashions</u> a fireplace from clay and metal.

   What does it mean to *fashion* something?
   - ○ **a.** to make it
   - ○ **b.** to light it
   - ○ **c.** to dig it up
   - ○ **d.** to fix it

7. Sam begins <u>harvesting</u> hickory nuts when he sees the squirrels eating them.

   What does Sam begin doing?
   - ○ **a.** cooking the nuts
   - ○ **b.** tasting the nuts
   - ○ **c.** gathering the nuts
   - ○ **d.** crushing the nuts

Selection Tests

ANSWER KEY

THEME 1

Selection 1

Earthquake Terror

Sample answers provided for questions 1 and 2.

1. The title of the story and the illustrations helped me make the prediction. I can infer that an earthquake makes loud noises. *(Strategy Focus: Predict/Infer)* (2.5 points)
2. Jonathan lies beside Abby. The ground trembles again and Jonathan wonders if the tree will crush them. The woods become quiet. *(sequence of events)* (2.5)
3. **b.** Abby notices a cut on her knee. *(sequence of events)* (1)
4. **c.** an island campground *(story structure)* (1)
5. **a.** Moose senses the changes in the earth. *(cause/effect and predict/infer)* (1)
6. **b.** undulating *(key vocabulary)* (1)
7. **a.** the striking of one object against another *(key vocabulary)* (1)

Assessment Tip: Total 10 points

Selection 2

Eye of the Storm: Chasing Storms with Warren Faidley

Sample answers provided for questions 1 and 2.

1. I asked this question, "With so much movement going on, how does Warren know whether his pictures will turn out?" The last sentence tells me that he doesn't really know until he sees the photographs. *(Strategy Focus: Question)* (2.5 points)
2. I expect an answer to the heading's question. After Warren takes his photos, he sells them to magazines, newspapers, advertisements, and films. *(text organization)* (2.5)
3. **b.** The headings tell the time and place of each entry. *(text organization)* (1)
4. **a.** *It sounded as if the sky were being torn apart.* *(fact/opinion)* (1)
5. **a.** Warren rides a bicycle into a dust whirlwind. *(sequence of events)* (1)
6. **b.** collide *(key vocabulary)* (1)
7. **a.** spin *(key vocabulary)* (1)

Assessment Tip: Total 10 points

Selection 3

Volcanoes

Sample answers provided for questions 1 and 2.

1. I wasn't sure that I understood how volcanoes form in the places where two plates meet until I studied the map on page 89. *(Strategy Focus: Monitor/Clarify)* (2.5 points)
2. Shield volcanoes have broad, gentle slopes. Cinder cone volcanoes look like upside-down ice cream cones. Composite volcanoes, or strato-volcanoes, are formed from layers of lava, ashes, and cinders. Dome volcanoes, which are dome-shaped, are formed by slow-moving lava. *(categorize/classify)* (2.5)
3. **b.** the Pacific Ocean *(categorize/classify)* (1)
4. **b.** strato-volcanoes *(categorize/classify)* (1)
5. **c.** *The eruption of Mount St. Helens was the most destructive in the history of the United States. (topic/main idea)* (1)
6. **c.** charred bits of rock *(key vocabulary)* (1)
7. **d.** melted rock *(key vocabulary)* (1)

Assessment Tip: Total 10 points

ANSWER KEY

THEME 2

Selection 1

Michelle Kwan: Heart of a Champion

Sample answers provided for questions 1 and 2

1. Yes, I like the way Michelle Kwan speaks in a natural style. It makes me feel included and keeps me interested. *(Strategy Focus: Evaluate)* (2.5 Points)
2. In Senior skating competitions, the "long program" is four minutes for women and four-and-a-half minutes for men. *(fact and opinion)* (2.5)
3. **c.** *Most skaters have really ugly feet. (fact and opinion)* (1)
4. **d.** *Each skater has two programs for competitions. (fact and opinion)* (1)
5. **a.** She tells the events in order. *(text organization)* (1)
6. **a.** take part in a contest *(key vocabulary)* (1)
7. **d.** They are necessary. *(key vocabulary)* (1)

Assessment Tip: Total 10 Points

Selection 2

La Bamba

Sample answers provided for questions 1 and 2

1. Manuel mouths the words of "La Bamba." He starts to dance. Then the record sticks. He keeps pantomiming. The record stops and Manuel runs off. *(Strategy Focus: Summarize)* (2.5 Points)
2. When Benny hits a high note on his trumpet during practice, Manuel drops his record. This is why the record sticks during Manuel's performance. *(story structure)* (2.5)
3. **c.** Manuel's "La Bamba" record gets stuck. *(story structure)* (1)
4. **d.** He yearns for the limelight. *(story structure)* (1)
5. **b.** People tell him that they liked his act. *(story structure)* (1)
6. **c.** clapping *(key vocabulary)* (1)
7. **d.** a natural ability *(key vocabulary)* (1)

Assessment Tip: Total 10 Points

ANSWER KEY

The Fear Place

Sample answers provided for questions 1 and 2

1. Doug respects the abilities of animals and thinks of Charlie as a friend. He also has told himself to think of the ledge as a chalk line. He is thinking more positively. *(Strategy Focus: Predict/Infer)* (2.5 Points)

2. Yes. Doug would still be focused on rescuing his brother, and he has been using his own positive thinking to keep going. *(predicting outcomes)* (2.5)

3. **b.** Doug will feel much more sure of himself on the way back. *(predicting outcomes)* (1)

4. **c.** He is trying to keep his mind from worrying. *(making inferences)* (1)

5. **b.** chalk line on the sidewalk *(noting details)* (1)

6. **a.** troubled *(key vocabulary)* (1)

7. **d.** careful *(key vocabulary)* (1)

Assessment Tip: Total 10 Points

Mae Jemison: Space Scientist

Sample answers provided for questions 1 and 2.

1. I didn't understand about biofeedback. I reread the parts about the problems using medicine for space-sickness, and about meditation. The photograph helped me picture the experiment. *(Strategy Focus: Monitor/Clarify)* (2.5 Points)

2. *Mae Jemison: Space Scientist* is about a woman named Mae Jemison who was the first African American female astronaut. *(topic/main idea)* (2.5)

3. **c.** Jemison flew in a special training jet that simulates zero gravity. *(topic/main idea)* (1)

4. **a.** Mae Jemison graduated from Stanford University. *(sequence of events)* (1)

5. **b.** lawyer *(categorize/classify)* (1)

6. **c.** able to be used again *(key vocabulary)* (1)

7. **d.** made 127 trips around Earth *(key vocabulary)* (1)

Assessment Tip: Total 10 Points

ANSWER KEY

THEME 3

Selection 1

And Then What Happened, Paul Revere?

Sample answers provided for questions 1 and 2.

1. I like the way she uses humor to show that although he is famous, Revere made mistakes like other people. (*Strategy Focus: Evaluate*) (2.5 Points)

2. I think she wrote to inform readers about the beginning of the American Revolution and to entertain readers by telling a story about historical events. (*author's point of view*) (2.5)

3. **b.** Paul Revere played an important role in the American Revolution. (*author's point of view*) (1)

4. **c.** excitement (*making generalizations*) (1)

5. **b.** They were rapid and made few or no stops. (*key vocabulary*) (1)

6. **a.** They were against it. (*key vocabulary*) (1)

7. **c.** freight (*key vocabulary*) (1)

Assessment Tip: Total 10 Points

Selection 2

Katie's Trunk

Sample answers provided for questions 1 and 2.

1. Katie runs back into the house and hears men coming to the door. She hides in her mother's wedding trunk. John Warren opens the trunk and realizes that someone is inside it. He leads the other rebels out of the house. (*Strategy Focus: Summarize*) (2.5 Points)

2. She becomes angry thinking about John Warren and Reuben Otis hurting her family's home and possessions, and feels she has to do something. (*cause and effect*) (2.5)

3. **b.** She hears rebels coming in the door. (*cause and effect*) (1)

4. **b.** He wants Katie to be able to breathe. (*cause and effect*) (1)

5. **d.** Many neighbors and former friends won't speak to them. (*problem solving*) (1)

6. **a.** skirmish (*key vocabulary*) (1)

7. **b.** looked (*key vocabulary*) (1)

Assessment Tip: Total 10 Points

Selection 3

James Forten

Sample answers provided for questions 1 and 2.

1. I could ask, "Why was it important that Africans found work in Philadelphia?" One reason work was important is that it allowed Africans to purchase their freedom. (*Strategy Focus: Question*) (2.5 Points)

2. First they loaded gunpowder into a gun and tamped it down. Then they put a cannonball into the barrel and pushed it against the powder. Last, they ignited the powder. (*following directions*) (2.5)

3. **b.** a man who helped fight for America (*topic/main idea*) (1)

4. **b.** James Forten was not a hero, but he fought well for his country. (*author's viewpoint*) (1)

5. **a.** *Sometimes he heard talk about naval battles, and he tried to imagine what they must have been like.* (*topic/main idea*) (1)

6. **c.** supported his plans (*key vocabulary*) (1)

7. **d.** prisoners (*key vocabulary*) (1)

Assessment Tip: Total 10 Points

ANSWER KEY

THEME 4

Selection 1

Mariah Keeps Cool

Sample answers provided for questions 1 and 2.

1. Lynn's mother is determined. She tells Lynn that she has taken time off from work so they can do something special. She suggests going to the bookstore, and Lynn wants books. *(Strategy Focus: Predict/Infer)* (2.5 Points)

2. Mariah tells Denise to hide and tells the other girls to sit on the edge of the pool and splash their feet. Brandon pretends to begin swimming practice and orders Lynn to leave. *(problem solving)* (2.5)

3. **b.** She asks her mother to send Lynn on an errand. *(problem solving)* (1)

4. **b.** She knows that Lynn will wonder why she is there. *(drawing conclusions)* (1)

5. **d.** in Mariah's yard *(story structure: summarizing)* (1)

6. **c.** to make something look pretty *(key vocabulary)* (1)

7. **d.** a party *(key vocabulary)* (1)

Assessment Tip: Total 10 Points

Selection 2

Mom's Best Friend

Sample answers provided for questions 1 and 2.

1. On page 377, I read that Ursula was nervous when Mom held the harness. I wasn't sure what a dog's harness looked like, but the pictures on pages 376 and 379 showed me the long handle of the harness and how Mom holds it. Those pictures helped me understand. *(Strategy Focus: Monitor/Clarify)* (2.5 Points)

2. Ursula is a German Shepherd, with dark and light markings and pointed ears. She is smaller than Marit was. She is sometimes keyed-up, or acts cute, and she likes children. *(noting details)* (2.5)

3. **b.** She jumps up on them and nearly knocks them over. *(noting details)* (1)

4. **d.** Mom does not let Ursula go outside for two weeks. *(following directions)* (1)

5. **a.** Mom scolds Ursula and asks the stranger not to pet her. *(problem solving)* (1)

6. **a.** comes naturally *(key vocabulary)* (1)

7. **c.** learned *(key vocabulary)* (1)

Assessment Tip: Total 10 Points

ANSWER KEY

Yang the Second and Her Secret Admirers

Sample answers provided for questions 1 and 2.

1. I could ask, "Why was the second part of the trick difficult for Yingtao, Third Sister, and Kim to arrange?" The answer is that they don't see Paul or his family very often. *(Strategy Focus: Question)* (2.5 Points)

2. They both like baseball, have sisters, and are Asian American. They are different because Yingtao is younger than Paul and goes to elementary school while Paul goes to high school. *(compare and contrast)* (2.5)

3. **a.** She used to have lots of friends. Now she has very few friends. *(compare and contrast)* (1)

4. **c.** The dinosaur was roaring too loudly. *(cause and effect)* (1)

5. **b.** a violin *(compare and contrast)* (1)

6. **c.** her Chinese traditions *(key vocabulary)* (1)

7. **c.** a play with singing *(key vocabulary)* (1)

Assessment Tip: Total 10 Points

Dear Mr. Henshaw

Sample answers provided for questions 1 and 2.

1. I would reread the part where Leigh describes the visit from his friend Barry. It makes me happy to read that Leigh has a new friend. I also think the part about the sign on Leigh's room is funny. *(Strategy Focus: Evaluate)* (2.5 Points)

2. I can tell Leigh is happy because he sounds proud of himself when he thinks about being called an author. Also, he wants to tell his Dad about the day and he sounds excited when he writes to Mr. Henshaw about his story. *(making inferences)* (2.5)

3. **b.** Writing helps him sort through his feelings about things. *(making inferences)* (1)

4. **a.** She is an honest woman. (making judgments) (1)

5. **b.** Writers should write about things they feel strongly about. *(making inferences)* (1)

6. **a.** his experiences *(key vocabulary)* (1)

7. **b.** a description *(key vocabulary)* (1)

Assessment Tip: Total 10 Points

ANSWER KEY

THEME 5

Selection 1

A Boy Called Slow

Sample answers provided for questions 1 and 2.

1. Slow could ride well, and he was very strong. He was known as a determined and courageous person. He also wanted to earn a name that was equal to his father's. *(Strategy Focus: Predict/Infer)* (2.5 points)

2. Slow is strong, determined, courageous, and kind. Like his father, he can understand some of what the animals say. Slow also shares a name with his father. *(compare/contrast)* (2.5)

3. **b.** He is a leader of his people. *(drawing conclusions)* (1)

4. **a.** He is stronger. *(drawing conclusions)* (1)

5. **a.** Sitting Bull *(noting details)* (1)

6. **c.** a tradition or way *(key vocabulary)* (1)

7. **c.** raid *(key vocabulary)* (1)

Assessment Tip: Total 10 points

Selection 2

Pioneer Girl

Sample answers provided for questions 1 and 2.

1. I could ask: "What did the McCance family store in their house and cellar during the winter?" The answer is that they stored foods such as beans, corn, onions, pumpkins, and potatoes. *(Strategy Focus: Question)* (2.5 points)

2. The poster uses phrases such as *Great central belt of population, commerce, and wealth* to convince the people that the area will quickly become populated. *(propaganda)* (2.5)

3. **a.** He always looks at the bright side of things. *(drawing conclusions)* (1)

4. **d.** makes new friends as more people settle nearby *(predicting outcomes)* (1)

5. **a.** to make readers feel that they could become rich *(propaganda)* (1)

6. **a.** a pioneer family's farmhouse, buildings, and land *(key vocabulary)* (1)

7. **d.** grassy soil *(key vocabulary)* (1)

Assessment Tip: Total 10 points

ANSWER KEY

Black Cowboy, Wild Horses

Sample answers provided for questions 1 and 2.

1. I think that he does a good job. For example, Lester shows the reader that this is a dangerous situation when he writes that the horses "whinnied and pranced nervously." *(Strategy Focus: Evaluate)* (2.5 points)
2. I admire Bob's survival skills and his love of the natural world, because these are skills and values that seem to be disappearing in today's world. *(making judgments)* (2.5)
3. **c.** He wants the horses to get used to him being around. *(story structure)* (1)
4. **a.** He is brave. *(making judgments)* (1)
5. **d.** It takes special skills to track wild mustangs. *(author's point of view)* (1)
6. **d.** They moved nervously. *(key vocabulary)* (1)
7. **d.** bluff *(key vocabulary)* (1)

Assessment Tip: Total 10 points

Elena

Sample answers provided for questions 1 and 2.

1. Elena finds Pancho Villa there with his men. He asks if this is the home of Pablo, the sombrero maker. She replies that it is and gives him a sombrero. This delights Pancho Villa, who pays her for the hat and puts a guard outside the house. *(Strategy Focus: Summarize)* (2.5 points)
2. When the soldiers come to town, Elena hides Esteban and the horses. When the family reaches California, she runs a boarding house. These events show that she is resourceful and wants to protect her family. *(story structure/summarizing)* (2.5)
3. **b.** Pablo's horse falls down a ravine. *(story structure/summarizing)* (1)
4. **b.** Esteban picks fruit and Elena runs a boardinghouse. *(problem solving)* (1)
5. **a.** It is completely destroyed. *(story structure/summarizing)* (1)
6. **b.** his condolences *(key vocabulary)* (1)
7. **b.** It was transformed. *(key vocabulary)* (1)

Assessment Tip: Total 10 points

ANSWER KEY

THEME 6

Selection 1

The Grizzly Bear Family Book

Sample answers provided for questions 1 and 2.

1. I like the first-person point of view because it makes the author's descriptions of the bears seem more real to the reader. *(Strategy Focus: Evaluate)* (2.5 Points)
2. Mother bears care for their cubs in much the same way that humans care for their babies. *(making generalizations)* (2.5)
3. **a.** *People have such fearful images of bears.* *(making generalizations)* (1)
4. **d.** Alaskan animals are interesting to photograph. *(making generalizations)* (1)
5. **c.** *One bear may consume 200,000 berries in a single day!* *(fact/opinion)* (1)
6. **c.** a region that is in its natural state *(key vocabulary)* (1)
7. **d.** with wariness *(key vocabulary)* (1)

Assessment Tip: Total 10 Points

Selection 2

The Golden Lion Tamarin Comes Home

Sample answers provided for questions 1 and 2.

1. Scientists at the zoo use the notes to help teach captive tamarins how to live in the wild. If I did not understand this at first, I could reread the whole paragraph. *(Strategy Focus: Monitor/Clarify)* (2.5 Points)
2. When the title says that "the golden tamarin comes home," it means that tamarins are being taken back to live in the wild. *(topic/main idea/supporting details)* (2.5)
3. **a.** *These animals do not have the skills to survive in the wild on their own.* *(topic/main idea/supporting details)* (1)
4. **c.** *Some die by eating poisonous fruits or snakes.* *(topic/main idea/supporting details)* (1)
5. **c.** *Each carries a canteen and a machete on a belt, as well as a backpack with food, rain gear, a snakebite kit, and mosquito repellent.* *(making generalizations)* (1)
6. **a.** captive tamarins *(key vocabulary)* (1)
7. **d.** dilemma *(key vocabulary)* (1)

Assessment Tip: Total 10 Points

ANSWER KEY

My Side of the Mountain

Sample answers provided for questions 1 and 2.

1. Sam leaps up, shouts, and slips on nuts that the animals have thrown everywhere. He chases the raccoons out, is sprayed by a skunk, and is surprised by a fox. Frightful is alarmed by the excitement. Sam adds wood to the fire and makes noises to make the other animals leave. *(Strategy Focus: Summarize)* (2.5 Points)

2. He sticks with a task until it is completed. He solves problems by trying different solutions. *(drawing conclusions)* (2.5)

3. **b.** He respects wild animals. *(drawing conclusions)* (1)

4. **b.** likes birds *(drawing conclusions)* (1)

5. **d.** cutting out more knotholes in the tree *(following directions)* (1)

6. **a.** to make it *(key vocabulary)* (1)

7. **c.** gathering the nuts *(key vocabulary)* (1)

Assessment Tip: Total 10 Points